HEALTH CARE CO-OPS IN UGANDA

HEALTH CARE CO-OPS IN UGANDA

Effectively Launching
Micro Health Groups
in African Villages

GEORGE C. HALVORSON

The Permanente Press
Oakland, California • Portland, Oregon

Published 2007 by The Permanente Press
Oakland, California • Portland, Oregon

The Permanente Press is owned by The Permanente Federation, LLC
Oakland, California

HEALTH CARE CO-OPS IN UGANDA: EFFECTIVELY LAUNCHING
MICRO HEALTH GROUPS IN AFRICAN VILLAGES

11 10 09 08 07   1 2 3 4 5

ISBN-13: 978-0-9770463-1-7
ISBN-10: 0-9770463-1-1
Library of Congress Control Number: 2006935873

Book design by Lynette Leisure
Chapter page icon by Laura Janisse

Printed in the United States of America

To the team in Uganda and
at HealthPartners who made
this entire effort a success.
Thank you all.

Contents

Introduction 1

Chapter One: The Beginning 7

Chapter Two: Working Backwards 23

Chapter Three: Who Owns It? Who Runs It? 33

Chapter Four: The Devil's In the Details 41

Chapter Five: Hitting Our 10-Cent Target 63

Chapter Six: Paying the Providers 77

Chapter Seven: Provider/Plan Cooperation=Success 91

Chapter Eight: Heroes and Hard Workers Make It Happen . . 107

Chapter Nine: Keeping the Co-Op's Money Safe 119

Chapter Ten: The Model Evolves 123

Chapter Eleven: Selling Our Plan 131

Chapter Twelve: The Hospital on Bushenyi Hill 139

Epilogue 151

Acknowledgments 157

Index 163

Introduction

$\mathcal{W}$hen we opened up a new local health care cooperative in rural Uganda, the start of each local plan was usually a joyful celebration involving lots of people.

Community leaders spoke. Dancers danced. Village singers sang songs of welcome and praise. People wore their ceremonial clothes.

The high point of each celebration was always the actual handing out of ID cards. It was a fascinating contrast to what we were used to back home. In America, we simply mail health care ID cards to our members. It's very much a non-event. In the Uganda health care co-ops, it's a public ceremony. Each family's name is announced. The head of the family comes forward and publicly receives a plastic laminated card (with the family member names on the front and the family photo on the back). The head of the family then shakes hands with the leadership of both the co-op and the village, and is applauded. The applause is obviously enthusiastic — heartfelt. Very real. Why is that?

Why do people in Uganda applaud when health plan ID cards are handed out?

The Ugandan applause recognizes that an important event has just occurred. That new ID card allows that family, often for the very first time in their lives, to seek and receive needed health care without financial hardship. It allows family members to receive sufficient health care without bankrupting the family. Children with malaria, dysentery, and parasitic infections can use that ID card to receive basic, necessary medical care.

Many mothers in urban Uganda who bring deathly ill infants to the hospital register those children under false names. If the child dies, the mother often slips away without paying the bill. Why? Family survival. Hospital bills can easily bankrupt a family, forcing them to sell their only cow, hut, or their small plot of land. The World Bank estimates that more than 30 percent of poor third world families who experience a serious illness are financially destroyed by the cost of care. Their estimate might be light.

So those deliberately misnamed and sadly deceased Ugandan babies are generally buried near the unpaid hospital in unmarked graves — with no one from their families able to be on hand to mourn their passing. It's unspeakably sad.

That's why the families celebrate getting that ID card in hand. Talk to the Ugandan parents in those little health care co-ops and it takes only minutes to understand why starting micro health plans is important in Uganda.

Uganda is a poor country full of brave people. Per capita income is a mere $270 per year. AIDS, dysentery, malaria, and parasitic infections are common. The infant mortality rates are among the highest in the world. The health care infrastructure is tiny, fragile, unevenly distributed, and functionally uncoordinated. Almost no one is insured through the private sector, and the government simply can't afford to provide care to every person who needs it. The tiny health care co-ops we set up in Uganda were really the only available form of health coverage in the communities we served.

So why did HealthPartners, a multi-billion dollar United States health care plan headquartered in Minnesota, decide to help set up tiny health care co-ops in Uganda?

Because HealthPartners is, itself, a health care co-op — the largest health care co-op in the world.

Land O'Lakes, a sister co-op for dairy farms also headquartered in Minnesota, has a long history of going into developing countries to set up local dairy co-ops. Uganda is one of more than a dozen countries that have benefited from the Land O'Lakes outreach initiative over the past two decades.

About eight years ago, members of the Land O'Lakes African dairy co-op staff were meeting with the leaders of a small dairy co-op in Uganda. The dairy co-op was doing well — functioning cooperatively — collecting its milk together, processing it together, protecting the quality together, and selling the milk together at a good price. Farmers working together had better incomes. The local market had better milk. The co-op was also importing carefully selected bull semen from the United States to upgrade the local herds and increase the milk production levels of its cows. Antibiotics were also being made available by the co-op to help ailing members of the tiny cattle herds. The cows in that Ugandan village had never been so healthy or so productive.

One of the farmers at the meeting said to the Land O'Lakes staff, "We now have good veterinary care for our cattle. Is there any way we can also get medical care for our children?"

That question intrigued the Land O'Lakes staff. When they returned to Minnesota, they called HealthPartners and asked that same question. Could it be possible to set up health care co-ops in a third world country, maybe starting with a foundation of small, local dairy co-ops?

HealthPartners decided to explore that possibility. A team from HealthPartners went to Uganda to meet with the co-op leaders. Two doctors and two administrators made that first trip. We met with dozens of rural Ugandan co-op leaders in half a dozen locations, and we concluded that it was worth a try.

This book describes what the staff from HealthPartners has

learned and accomplished since that time. There are now working health care co-ops in Uganda. They are serving thousands of people in a dozen villages and rural communities. People are getting care that they wouldn't have gotten without the co-ops.

In a country with more than 27,000,000 people, that's just a tiny beginning. But, it is a start. The government of Uganda is watching closely to see if the approach can be expanded to other sites. The United States Agency for International Development, USAID, program has been incredibly supportive of the entire process. So have the local villages and caregivers. They have created true health care co-ops.

That's why HealthPartners is involved.

It's a cooperative thing to do. Co-ops tend to be a bit evangelical in their approach to the world. People who understand the co-op mentality know that the Land O'Lakes efforts to support developing nations' dairy farmers are very much in keeping with the worldwide tendency of co-ops to help other co-ops get started. HealthPartners is coming from that same perspective. That's how co-ops think: "If we can use some of the tools we've developed to help others go down a similar path, then, we co-ops believe, that's a reasonable thing for us to do. It fits our value system, and our cooperative commitment to helping others."

The approach HealthPartners is using in Uganda will not solve Uganda's health care problems. It will make life better for some Ugandans, however. Much better. Women will have prenatal care. Kids will survive dysentery and malaria. Diseases will be prevented for some people, and cured for others. Some people will be healthier. Not everyone — but some.

Is that enough?

One of my favorite stories is of a man walking down a beach early in the morning. As he looked down the shore, he saw another man in the distance walking toward him. The other man was regularly stooping over picking something up, and throwing it into the ocean.

As the men drew closer, the first man saw that the stranger was picking up shellfish and throwing them out to sea.

"What are you doing?" he asked. "Why are you throwing those shells into the water?"

"Because the tide invariably catches some shellfish and washes them ashore," the stranger replied. "They die on the shore, so I throw them back into the water."

The first man looked down the shore in both directions. There were shells far up and down the coast.

"It's hopeless," the first man said. "There are huge numbers of them. You're just one person. You can't possibly make a difference."

The second man bent over and picked up another shellfish. He held it for a second and then he threw it far out to sea. He looked at the first man and said softly, "Hey, it made a difference for that one."

What's the value of one human life? What's the value of one surviving child? What's the value of one mother being healthy enough to care for her family? What HealthPartners is doing in Uganda won't change the world. But it is making a difference. A real difference in real lives. That's good enough.

I wrote the first draft of this book just prior to leaving HealthPartners to move to Kaiser Permanente, the nation's largest non-profit health maintenance organization (HMO). I put the book on a shelf for the past couple of years because I had other priorities. But people kept asking about Uganda and the little health care co-ops there.

I was just in South Africa. A couple of people there who had heard about the Ugandan co-ops asked me, "Is there anything about the co-ops in writing? Do you have anything that describes how that project was done?"

People at the World Bank recently asked the same questions. The story has been the subject of a National Public Radio special and there were a few articles in various magazines — but each of those reports just told a few things about the project. They didn't explain it — or help share the learnings that have resulted.

So, I thought I'd bring the book back to life and make it available. HealthPartners is still doing wonderful things in Uganda, and the learnings from that effort deserve to be shared. Those co-ops have taken root. That's what co-ops aspire to — real rootings.

I actually wrote this book twice, once as an operational "how to" textbook, and once as a narrative story of what we did. This version combines the two approaches. My hope is that this combined approach might, in the long run, be more useful to more people. So, I blended the two books into this single description of the program.

Most of the pure textbook teachings and topics are included in this version, including product design, decisions, actuarial issues, governance structure, negotiations, operational theory, etc. They are just embedded a bit in the story of what we did.

I hope this version works for you, and that the book is useful to anyone thinking about setting up local, consumer- or provider-owned health plans in any setting. In the right place at the right time, health care co-ops can be a very workable way to finance and deliver health care.

George Halvorson
June 2006

Chapter One
The Beginning

It was pretty obvious pretty quickly that we Americans all had
a lot of learning to do before we aspired to do any teaching.

The Pearl of Africa

Following a visit to Uganda in 1907, Winston Churchill,
enamored of its stunning beauty, declared it "The Pearl of Africa."
Those of us from HealthPartners who spent time there would
agree. It's a beautiful country full of warm and friendly people.
Unfortunately, it faces many challenges economically, politically,
and health-wise. For you to better understand this whole health
care co-op story, you need to know a little bit more about this
spectacular country.

This country of almost 28 million people is located on the
equator in central and eastern Africa. For many years it was
part of the British Empire, achieving independence in 1962.
During the 1970s, Idi Amin, a vicious dictator, ruled the country for eight years. Uganda has also endured several decades of
intense tribal warfare, which has subsided to some degree in
the past decade.

Much of the country's wealth is concentrated in the capital city
of Kampala, which sits on the shores of Lake Victoria. But more

than a third of the population lives below the poverty line, with nine million people living on less than the equivalent of $1 a day.

A Country With Significant Health Care Needs

The original title for this book was "Malaria, Dysentery, Parasites, Bad Water, and Difficult Births — The Story of Ugandan Health Care Co-ops." That title, while descriptive, was far too long and had to be changed. But, the point of that title needs to be made.

Uganda is a country with significant health care needs — and the little health care co-ops we helped set up made a difference in very basic ways for the people who joined them. The health care situation in Uganda is not one that Americans are used to seeing.

Disease is an ever-present threat, and an estimated 4.1 percent of the population is thought to be HIV-positive. Cholera is also a major health threat, followed by dysentery and typhoid. Malaria also presents a constant threat, especially to young children. Intestinal parasites are a persistent problem, particularly to the very young. One third of Uganda's people will not live to see the age of 40. The government has hospitals in Kampala, but most Ugandans can't afford them, or can't get to them.

Nearly one third of the babies receiving care at the Nsambya Hospital in Kampala, Uganda are registered under false names. I was told that by one of the hospital administrators.

Why are the false names used? Because the parents of the infants have little or no money and can't afford to pay the hospital bill — particularly if the baby dies.

Most people in Uganda are breathtakingly poor. Per capita income is only about $270 a year.

The vast majority of families try to earn a living on tiny plots of land — growing yams or a green banana called "matooke," raising a few goats or chickens, and, when possible, milking a cow or two. Cattle are particularly valued. A Ugandan with a small cattle herd is considered to be well-to-do.

Only One Cow

Many families have only one cow. Milk from that cow provides food and is often the only dependable source of family cash. I've seen small children walk for miles every single day to pick enough clumps of grass from ditches, river bottoms, and badly overgrazed pastures to feed the sole family cow. They hand-carry that grass back to the cow. And, they also hand-carry buckets of water from the local stream or well for the cow to drink. The cow can be the primary source of the family economy. So, selling that cow in order to have enough money to pay a large hospital bill for a dead baby just plain doesn't make economic sense to many families. The rest of the family would lose its only ongoing access to cash without the cow.

So mothers of dying children often slip away into the night — leaving their hospitalized baby to die alone and be buried by strangers.

Health care in Uganda is a constant lesson in stark reality. Per capita expenditures on health care — from all government, private, and charitable sources — run about $1 per month. That is about $12 a year.

Twelve dollars is almost a rounding error on a monthly health care premium charged in the United States. An average monthly expense for Medicare recipients in many areas of the United States now exceeds $1,000 per person. Uganda spends $12 a year per person.

So why did HealthPartners, a large American health plan with nearly $2 billion in annual revenue in the United States, go to Uganda to start a health plan? It clearly wasn't because there was a wonderful business opportunity — or a chance to use American know-how to make local care more efficient and maybe save money in the process. It's darn hard to get more efficient than a total monthly per person health care expenditure of $1.

HealthPartners ended up in Uganda because Land O'Lakes,

one of America's largest dairy cooperatives, had started a program years ago to bring co-op approaches to developing countries. Land O'Lakes is one of the most recognizable names in butter in the United States. Begun as the Minnesota Cooperative Creameries in 1924, the company made its name by producing commercially prepared butter from fresh cream, rather than the sour cream previously used by creameries. Land O'Lakes — in a pure missionary spirit — has helped start dairy co-ops in more than a dozen countries. Uganda was one of those countries. Eight years ago, Land O'Lakes had already helped organize nearly 40 local dairy co-ops throughout Uganda.

One very positive result of co-ops organizing around milk production and sales was the ability of local farmers with small dairy herds to band together in a farmer-owned cooperative to purchase low-cost veterinary care for their cattle.

"If we can use this approach to get better medical care for our cows," one of the local co-op leaders asked the Land O'Lakes executive then in charge of Uganda co-ops, "then why can't we use the same approach somehow to also buy medical care for our children?"

HealthPartners, like Land O'Lakes, is a cooperative. It is, in fact, the largest consumer-run, consumer-governed health co-op in the world.

HealthPartners has also traditionally been a provider of health care services to Land O'Lakes employees and staff. A lot of Land O'Lakes employees are HealthPartners members.

So, when the question about providing some level of health care to children in equatorial African dairy co-ops was asked, members of the Land O'Lakes International staff set up a meeting with HealthPartners in snow-covered St. Paul, Minnesota to ask whether or not HealthPartners might be interested in bringing the co-op model of health care financing and care delivery to Africa. At that point, I was the President and CEO of HealthPartners, and

I was personally intrigued by the request. So were key members of our staff and our consumer-elected board of directors.

The HealthPartners leadership staff agreed to take a look at the situation, to see if we believed a co-op model might be useful or even possible in Uganda. Part of the co-op mentality is to help other co-ops get started, so the idea started on fertile ground.

Our own plan in Minnesota had, in fact, been inspired nearly 40 years ago by co-op "missionaries" from Seattle, Washington. The Seattle people had started their own consumer health co-op a decade earlier and were successful in building a plan based on patient needs and local consumer control. We, in turn, had helped start similar health care co-ops in several other American cities. So, there was a historical legacy in our organization — both for being helped by other co-ops and for helping other health care co-ops get underway.

Those historical health care co-op start-ups that had been supported by HealthPartners years ago had all been in Midwestern United States cities like Madison, Milwaukee, or St. Cloud, not exotic cities or towns like Kampala, Mbarara, or Kasizi.

We talked the issue over inside our organization. HealthPartners has always been led by its mission: "To improve the health of our members and our community." Our annual business plans were always put together in the context of that mission. In a number of cases, we had made investments and set up programs to help local people who were not our members, using, in those cases, a fairly broad local definition of community to determine who might be helped.

It took, however, a truly broad definition of "community" to stretch the HealthPartners' mission all the way out to Uganda. But, we decided it also had taken a relatively broad definition for Minnesotans to reach out to Kansas City. So, we decided to be, at least initially, fairly open-minded on that particular point of geographic distance. If we could actually help other health care co-ops get started, we thought that a global sense of community commitment might be relevant and appropriate to the HealthPartners mission.

The real issue, we decided, was to figure out whether or not the co-op model we believed in would actually be relevant or useful in Africa. That's not a decision we could make from the United States, so we decided that we ought to at least visit Uganda before making our decision on whether or not we could, and should, transplant the co-op approach to health care to that country. We decided that a small team of medical and administrative leaders should visit the Land O'Lakes sites in Uganda. The team would check out the local care system, talk to the people in the dairy co-ops, and then decide whether or not to make an attempt to bring a consumer-governed health plan model to Africa.

So, a small team from HealthPartners — Dr. Maureen Reed, Dr. Jim Hart, Scott Aebischer, and I — traveled to Uganda in September 1997 to meet with local co-op leaders and with a number of Ugandan caregivers. Drs. Reed and Hart were both highly skilled medical practitioners and community leaders who had prior experience delivering care through an African mission. Their insights into the local care situation proved invaluable. Plus, they also helped immensely in creating immediate credibility with local caregivers.

"Why Me?" He Asked

When I first approached Scott Aebischer, then the HealthPartners Vice President for Provider Contracting, with the idea of his participating as a key player in a new Uganda health plan project, he was very much taken aback. "Why me?" he asked. "What role would a contract negotiator play in Ugandan health care? Shouldn't the project lead be a doctor? Or a financial person? Or a public policy expert? Or a marketing person?"

Good questions. And easy to answer.

Years ago, in an earlier career phase, I had helped start an HMO in Jamaica. What I discovered at that time was that the bottom-line key to success for the Jamaica plan was successful provider contracting. Frankly, that should not surprise anyone who understands health plan operations. Without a care network, HMOs can't exist. That is always true. Scott was running provider contracting for HealthPartners and doing it really well. He is a gifted negotiator. People do deals with Scott and then, years later, they renew the deals. Anyone can do an initial deal. Renewals, however, take great competence and credibility. I believed then that the skill set needed to keep a United States-contracted care network thriving is pretty much the same skill set needed to start a brand new health plan provider network in a developing country. I still believe that.

Scott has been the rock and the foundation for the entire program. He was, to be entirely honest, not initially intrigued by the prospect of going to Uganda with me and our team to evaluate whether or not we should start a health plan there. As I noted, he had quite a few years of experience putting together deals with providers of care. He knew those issues inside out. He also knows just about every variation in financing models. He has the personal ability to build long-term, very amiable, win/win, trusting relationships that involve contracts that result in the delivery of care. The reason people continue to renew with Scott is because he's not out to gain advantage. He wants both parties to win — because that's what makes programs truly successful over time.

I felt strongly that if our Uganda effort was to have any chance of success, that entire skill set needed to be present in that program. So I twisted Scott's arm just slightly to get him to give the whole project a look. And he didn't disappoint me. He has dedicated long hours to the project, and has put together a great team of people that he has led with skill and grace. He did that in spite of having an increasingly responsible full-time day job at HealthPartners.

Before leaving the United States, we set a goal for our fact-finding mission. Our goal was to see if it was possible to establish some kind of self-perpetuating, locally governed, patient-focused, co-op-based health care program that would improve the quality, affordability, and accessibility of health care for Ugandans.

In the traditional true spirit of pure co-op missionary work, our objective was not to expand our own company. It was to help a similar organization get started.

We knew from day one that we were not looking at a business venture in the sense that HealthPartners expected to make money by running African health systems. But, it was very much a business-structured venture in the sense that the practical, clearly stated project goal was to help set up local programs that were financially viable, operationally functional, and able to stay in business on their own in Uganda after the Americans had all gone home.

We quickly discovered that Uganda is a country riddled with HIV/AIDS. Entire communities have been devastated and depopulated by HIV/AIDS. It is a country where very few women receive prenatal care. Malaria affects most of the population at least some of the time. Dysentery and various parasites sap the strength of children and adults alike.

Immunization levels are very low in many areas. Doctors and nurses are both in short supply. Most rural hospitals consider themselves to be fortunate if they have indoor plumbing. Many do not. Two of the first four hospitals we worked with who did have plumbing did not actually have hot water when the project started.

Medical equipment was in very short supply. One of the hospitals we visited on that first tour had its only piece of high-tech equipment — an antique X-ray machine — out of commission for more than two years. Doctors in that hospital set broken bones by skill and feel, unable to see the exact nature and location of any fractures or breaks.

For someone used to the massive, well-equipped infrastructure of United States health care, Uganda was a fascinating place to be. People delivered care — often good care — under the most challenging conditions imaginable. It was a real learning experience. We had to learn to see the local situation in the context of the local reality. That isn't always an easy thing to do.

In most rural Ugandan hospitals, for example, patients are expected to bring their own food. The hospital grounds are, therefore, littered with small cooking fires, set up by families to feed their bedridden kin.

Live Chickens

Live chickens could often be purchased near the hospital entryways. At first blush, to American eyes, having a lot of chickens by the hospital door appeared to be a real health hazard. But we soon learned that a live chicken was actually much less of a health risk than a dead chicken kept for any length of time in an unrefrigerated state in an equatorial climate, while the farmer waited patiently for a buyer. Also, from a safety perspective, if the chicken you were planning to buy for dinner was already dead, you really didn't know exactly why or how it had died. The cause of death can be an important thing to know if you intend to personally eat the bird.

It was pretty obvious pretty quickly that we Americans all had a lot of learning to do before we aspired to do any teaching.

The caregivers themselves were heroic people — overburdened, understaffed, underpaid, and attempting to deliver the best possible care under extremely trying circumstances.

For those of us used to United States hospitals and clinics, the contrast was stunning. We are wrapped completely in the very much under-appreciated security of our own American care system's stunningly sterile, technology-rich, safe, and well-designed, care-site cocoons. We Americans have no sense of how little of what we take for granted in our own system is readily available in most of the world.

Drs. Hart and Reed had actually been caregivers in Africa for a short time, and I had personally helped to set up a small, locally owned health plan in Jamaica over a decade earlier, so our team had some small sense of what we might expect. Once we got to rural Uganda, however, we discovered that the situation was even more challenging than we had feared.

What kept us from giving up and heading back in full retreat to Minnesota's modern medical comfort levels were the people of rural Uganda who spoke so eloquently about the need for the kind of program we had hoped to set up.

Consumer Leadership and Consumer Focus

Richard Bakojja, a Ugandan dairy farmer who also served as Land O'Lakes local chief of staff at that time, set up a series of meetings with key leaders and interested members from existing local dairy co-ops. As we traveled around the country over deeply rutted dirt roads in a well-worn Land Rover to various rural communities, we did a lot of learning. Richard had arranged for a dozen discussions with nearly 100 Ugandan dairymen. At those initial meetings, we described our American health plan. To help people understand the cooperative nature of our organization and who we were, we talked a good bit about our own plan's history — about our fragile and modest origin as a very small group of local Minnesota labor leaders and left-leaning university professors who had wanted, four decades before, to build an affordable, patient-focused, consumer-controlled alternative to for-profit, fee-for-service medicine. We talked about how our own very few first staff people in Minnesota brought light bulbs, lamps, tables, and chairs from their own homes to furnish our original tiny clinic. We talked about growing from that tiny, fragile cooperative seed to having more than 600,000 members and one of the largest medical groups in the

United States. We also talked about the power of consumer leadership and consumer focus. We talked about the value of member-elected health plan governance when it came to setting health policy and negotiating the best deals for our patients.

That message resonated with the Ugandan dairy farmers. They had already banded together to form dairy co-ops to create mutual collection sites and distribution systems for their milk. They already understood the potential power of cooperative action. They also already understood the improved price leverage that comes with volume purchasing. They wanted that power and mutual co-op leverage applied to their children's health.

Sitting in small, tin-roofed, rural Ugandan buildings with open, glass-free windows, we listened as speaker after speaker told stories of sick family members who had gone untreated for weeks or even months, because their families had no cash to pay the medical bill. Husbands told stories of wives dying in childbirth. Mothers told stories of children dying from malaria, parasites, or untreated intestinal infections.

The intensity of some of the speakers was almost intimidating. This wasn't an academic exercise for the people we talked to. It was a matter of life and death. Literally. It was an extremely serious topic for the people who spoke to us. Several of the local people made one particular point in response to our presentation. They wanted us to be very real as well. As one rural co-op leader said just before the noon break at the very first large meeting, "The cooperative health care dream you are telling us about is wonderful. We want to be able to bring our children and our wives to the doctors without fear of losing everything we own financially. It's a wonderful dream. But don't just give us a pretty, American speech and get our hopes up. Don't make promises you can't keep. This is too important to us to be told about this wonderful thing while you just leave here, get on an airplane, and go back to America and forget us. If you are serious about a health care co-op, let's talk. If you are not serious, then go away and don't waste our time."

The attendees at that particular meeting almost filled a large, open air meeting room in a field next to a co-op milk collection center. We could see cows out the window and smell fresh (and not-so-fresh) milk. Some of the people had come from 10 to 15 miles away. With no public transportation, the audience came on bicycle or on foot — with most people walking through fields, hills, and jungle to hear the American health care co-op people talk about care and the incredible, almost unbelievable possibility of mutually banding together to make that care affordable and accessible. The hard-earned credibility of the local Land O'Lakes staff had filled those rooms with interested local people ready to listen. The subject matter got people dreaming about what might happen if our stories about cooperative health care turned out to be true.

So, during the noon break, eating steamed goat cooked in banana leaves and covered with peanut-flavored mashed matooke, our small team huddled to see what our response might be to these challenges. We knew that we were far too early in the process to make any promises about actually creating a Ugandan health program — but we were impressed and moved by the

Bringing matooke to town to sell.

intense interest in setting something up. And, we didn't want to let the momentum that was forming simply fade away. So after lunch, we told the group a message that we then repeated to everyone else we dealt with on that trip.

We said, "We can't promise you a program. We need to learn much more before we can do that. What we will promise is that if we can figure out a way to set up cooperative health plans in Uganda, we will then try very hard to make that happen. But, that will then require your help to be successful. The new health care co-ops will be yours — run by you and owned by you. So, we need to know — if we can develop a good and workable co-op design and plan, will you support a health care co-op and will you help make it happen? Will you run it if we help you get it started? That will be the key to your success. This needs to be your plan — not ours. It needs to be run by you — not us. We can help, but only you can make it happen. Is this important enough to you that you will be willing to do the hard work necessary to make this dream real?"

They told us in return, "If you give us a good plan, we will make it happen." We heard that at every meeting. We believed it. We believed that their commitment was very real, because the need was so great — and that has, in fact, proven to be true. The local co-ops do run themselves and the people in those co-ops actually do the hard work to keep them running — because the need for health care is felt so strongly by people who have suffered so much without it.

Uganda is a country about the size of Oregon, with 40 tribal languages, built around three major language groups. At each dairy co-op meeting, we had translators standing next to us to translate our points into the various local dialects. At this initial meeting, there were two translators — both were local dairy co-op leaders — each translating our comments into their own tribal language. The only language spoken consistently across the entire country is

English, a vestigial remnant of the British Empire. So, most people in Uganda with any education speak at least some English.

At the point in the first meeting later that afternoon when we asked our questions in English about local support, most members of that first audience didn't even wait for the translation. They nodded vigorously and said, "Yes, yes, we will help. We will make it happen. We will support the plan."

After the meeting, the local Anglican Bishop — a Ugandan from a nearby village who had heard about our morning presentation and sat in, uninvited, on the afternoon session — came up to us, welcomed us to his town, and said quietly, "Don't disappoint my people." The comment, made with a quiet smile, triggered the emotional response in our group that I expect he was seeking. We were starting to feel pretty committed ourselves.

So, in a nutshell, we four Minnesotans, far from home, had talked ourselves into an interesting dilemma. In a country with breathtakingly minimal cash flow, a fragile and obviously inadequate health care infrastructure, no accessible government funding for health, and a generally sick and impoverished population, we were committing to figuring out how to build a health plan model that had some reasonable probability of both short-term success and long-term survival.

No small task.

Local Problems Need Local Solutions

Years earlier, I had personally helped start a health plan in Jamaica. On my first trip to that country, I had assumed — in error — that the same issues that were most relevant to United States health plans would, of course, be equally applicable in Jamaica. At that point, most United States health plans succeeded financially in large part by eliminating unnecessary hospital days, and cutting out expensive and unneeded Friday admissions for Monday surgery, for example. So, I focused immediately on reducing hospital costs in Jamaica. It was a bit embarrassing. A hospital day in Jamaica turned out to be less than $10 in average costs, and lengths of stay in hospitals were already very short for most people because most people didn't like being in Jamaican hospitals. That well-tested, hospital-focused American approach to reducing health care costs actually had no value in Jamaica. It turned out, after a little study, that the real cost driver for Jamaican health care was prescription drugs. The winning strategy we ultimately developed for our Jamaican health plan was to buy pharmaceuticals in volume and also to import very low-cost, generic drugs directly, bypassing the local major Jamaican pharmacy retailers who almost exclusively bought and distributed unaffordably expensive brand name drugs. In the United States at that time, drugs were less than 4 percent of total health care costs. In Jamaica, they were over 60 percent. So that's where we had to focus our problem-solving skills. One size solutions do not fit all countries. I had learned quickly *not* to assume that all American solutions worked everywhere. Local problems need local solutions. So, rather than simply applying American solutions to Uganda, we focused entirely on what was actually needed in Uganda.

Chapter Two
Working Backwards

A dime is a tough target.

$\mathcal{W}$e started our serious thinking about the Ugandan health care co-ops by setting up some macro goals for the Ugandan program. As Stephen Covey so wisely says in *The Seven Habits of Highly Effective People*, "Begin with the end in mind." We first asked ourselves what objectives we needed to reach for the program to be a success.

Then we asked ourselves, what strategies would be needed to accomplish those goals? What tools did we Americans have in our total health plan/health insurance/health provider toolkit that could be used to actually accomplish those goals in Uganda?

Our team first met with the local Land O'Lakes people to work through the goals. And then we met separately as a team to figure out a first draft of the strategies that might work. We knew we had to fit our specific strategies to the actual Ugandan situation or we would have no chance of success

In the process, we set nine initial goals — goals that were directly relevant to Uganda and to the people who might form health care co-ops in that beautiful, but incredibly impoverished, country. You might find our set of goals useful if you have any interest in starting a similar plan in some other setting. We didn't take any goals or expectations for granted. We wanted all of the key goals clearly understood and on the table.

Goals for the Uganda Program

We wanted to create a system that would:

1. Provide affordable care
2. Assure predictable/budgetable costs
3. Provide dependable/available care
4. Be as theft-proof as possible
5. Assure local governance and local member control
6. Be self-sustaining and self-perpetuating
7. Be actuarially and financially viable
8. Be easy to administer, and
9. Provide an approach people would trust.

---

1) Affordable Care — We knew from meeting with the people both in the mountain villages and in the larger cities that affordability had to top the list. An unaffordable plan would serve no purpose, and would be a complete waste of everybody's time.

2) Budgetable Costs — When people have an extremely slender cash flow and absolutely no cash reserves, then any major, unexpected cost can entirely disrupt and destroy their total financial status. Paying for a routine course of care for malaria, for example, while cheap by United States standards, had the potential to wipe out a Ugandan family's cash resources and possibly require the sale of an essential and irreplaceable family asset to pay the bill.

It wasn't enough to negotiate lower prices for incidents of care. We needed a payment model that would allow each Ugandan family to budget health care expenses. In the United States, health plans generally add value for their members by using mass volume purchasing leverage to negotiate significant discounts for care. Those negotiated fee discounts keep American health plan premium levels lower for members. We knew that the discount-fee model alone would not suffice in Uganda, because even a 20 percent or 30 percent discount for local fee-for-service care didn't solve that basic affordability or unexpected-expense problem. Even a deeply discounted fee could create an immediate cost that represented a major negative financial hit to a patient if it came at an unexpected time, or, if the family had to pay the money all at once. Affordable care, we decided, was a two-part package. It had to mean both lower-cost care and care costs that could be predictably and affordably spread out over longer periods of time. Rather than large invoices for major illnesses, we needed care costs spread out over monthly payments. The term we used with the new co-ops was *budgeted* costs. We needed monthly budgeted costs that were affordable and not changeable, regardless of health care needs.

3) Dependable and Available Care — Clearly, in a setting with minimal transportation facilities, people needed nearby care they could get to by walking. In one setting, Kasizi, we learned about large, ornate, almost throne-like, woven-wicker stretchers designed to carry corpses — in other words, wicker hearses. The people also used some of these as mobile ambulances to carry very sick people to the hospital. On our first trip to Uganda, we almost ran over one coming around a sharp turn on a hillside. Four men were carrying the intricately woven, reed hearse through the hills to the hospital gate with a very sick woman reclining on the platform. That, obviously, was not a transportation mechanism that would allow the hospital to be located a long way away from where people live. Again, local reality prevailed. We recognized that any local health plan we designed that required people to travel 30 or 40 miles for care would never work in a setting where the local ambulance service relied on retrofitted pallbearers with sandal-clad feet for locomotion. We needed to find a way to provide very local care that patients could access when they needed it. We set that as a goal.

4) A Theft-Free System — Our fourth goal was to create a totally theft-proof system, if possible. During our initial visit, we heard several stories about scams set up in various places by people purporting to sell some version of life or health insurance. The scammers then simply stole the money and disappeared. Those experiences left scars. They also served as a warning to us. In a country where cash is an incredibly scarce commodity, we didn't want to create an insurance model that involved large sums of cash accumulated and held in a tempting situation by anyone, in any place, at any time. We wanted to design a co-op model that served, first and foremost, to forestall temptation. We also wanted a model with obvious, logical, practical, and transparent cash-protection safety features that we could easily explain to the co-op members. We knew each local co-op would need to know exactly what steps we would take to keep their money safe.

5) Local Governance and Local Member Control — As a member-owned co-op ourselves, we wanted to help other member-owned co-ops get started. Land O'Lakes had exactly the same values and objectives. We wanted to establish a plan run by local people for local people. Over time, the Ugandan project has developed a couple of other local health plan governance options and organizational models that serve to supplement the pure co-op approach. Most of the non-co-op plans are run by local health care providers. That's also a good model. Provider-run health plans can fill a real need in a number of settings. But, our initial goal, a purely co-op model, remains the HealthPartners' preferred model.

6) Self-Sustainable and Self-Perpetuating — Ugandans use a somewhat cynical expression about health care that translates roughly to "when the white faces leave, the care goes away." We saw completely abandoned clinic sites with goats sleeping in the old exam rooms. We didn't want to build a model that required us or any other outsider to stay in Uganda forever. We set a goal of building a model that worked so well, so elegantly, and with such obviously transparent value that it could and would run without us. Each local program had to be logical, simple to explain, simple to set up, and easy to run.

We aimed to eliminate all unnecessary costs and process steps. A complex model requiring constant external high-tech/high-maintenance attention and a lot of ongoing operational support clearly would not work. Or at least, it wouldn't meet our simplicity goal. We decided at that very early point in the process to make sure our entire staff in Uganda was Ugandan. We didn't want a plan that relied on either imported staff or absentee core management. We wanted to train a local staff that would remain in place after we had completed our job and gone home. We decided that we would send Minnesotans to Uganda for temporary stays only. When necessary, we would bring Ugandan staff to Minnesota for training.

Some international health care experts initially criticized that approach, but it has actually worked well — except for the time we flew two key Ugandans to Minnesota for briefings and training in the middle of winter. We thought they might enjoy the wonder of Christmas in Minnesota. We thought that the snow would surprise and delight them. We were wrong. Snow did not amuse them. They hated it, in fact. On their first evening with us, they took a long walk in the snow. When they came back, they told us their resignations would be on our desk in the morning if we ever brought them into weather that painfully cold again. So, we flipped our Minnesota-based training schedule for our Ugandan staff exclusively to summers.

Part of the self-sustaining concept in our plan required us to not provide any charity care. We all found that a particularly painful decision to make. But, we were told by our Ugandan friends, by USAID, and by local experts whose opinion we valued, if we turned any part of the co-op program into a pure giveaway or "gifting" process, we would potentially destroy it as a self-sustaining operation. If we simply donated free X-ray machines, for example, then co-op members would see our most valuable role as a source of gifts, and the local plans and care sites would become gift-dependent rather than self-sufficient.

That was an extremely difficult point for us to accept, and no other decision that we made was as painful as that one. In several settings, we knew that we relatively well-to-do Americans could fix some local care-related problems very quickly with a check — but if we did that, we would run the risk of polluting and even crippling the prospect of each local co-op program going forward in perpetuity on its own steam. So, in the interest of sustainability, we made the extremely difficult decision not to do anything that smacked of pure charity — at least not where we were setting up co-ops.

To be honest, we may have slipped a bit on that non-charity point in a non-co-op setting or two, but not with the actual co-ops.

Each of us included in the project has felt pain from that particular decision at one point or another, but we continue to believe it was an important decision to make for the particular work we were doing.

This is not meant in any way as a negative reflection on charity work. Charity work is wonderful, and we encourage others to do that important work as often as possible. But our clear mission, and our overarching goal, was to set up self-sustaining care systems. So, we held ourselves to that pure, self-sustaining standard. We brought organizational expertise to Uganda, but not operating room equipment.

7) Actuarially and Financially Viable — We all agreed the plan had to be actuarially and financially viable, both immediately and over time. Actuarial viability may seem like an academic, insurance-industry-insider type of priority, but it's really another key to any program like this succeeding. Actuarial soundness is, in fact, a critical success factor that has to be clearly understood and carefully managed for any program of this type to survive over time. Plans could not be sustainable and self-perpetuating unless they were actuarially sound.

What does *actuarially sound* mean? Remember, local health care co-ops are actually a form of insurance. Insurance always depends on a spread of risk. That concept applies to all kinds of insurance. For example, in order to have enough money to pay out benefits to those people who die, life insurance companies need to have a lot of living people paying premiums. That is where the money comes from — the people who live and pay premiums.

Those same realities apply to health insurance. No privately funded health plan anywhere in the world can be financially viable if people who are already deathly ill are the only ones to ever enroll in the plan. Think of how insurance actually works. Successful insurers spread risk across populations of people. Life insurance companies in the United States don't allow people dying of cancer to buy $1 million policies on their deathbed. Why not? Because the only way the life insurance companies could ever break even in that case would be to charge a $1 million premium to that $1 million cancer patient. That's why life insurers try to sell their coverage to people who will live long and pay a lot of premium for a long time before they die. If people could wait until they were almost dead before buying life insurance, why would anyone buy insurance earlier?

Not to belabor the point, but life insurance companies obviously have to enroll quite a few people who pay their premiums without dying immediately. Likewise, fire insurance companies in the United States do not sell coverage to people in burning houses. They don't authorize local fire truck drivers to sell their company's fire insurance policies to desperate homeowners at actual fire sites. It takes premium dollars from a lot of houses that aren't burning to pay for the houses that do burn. That's called spreading risk.

Health care insurers have that same need to spread risk. In the United States, when an insured premature baby requires $1 million in care, the cost of that $1 million is actually parceled out. That high care cost adds to the monthly premium of every other member of the health plan covering that baby. If a plan has a million members, each member pays $1 in premium to cover that baby. That's how insurance companies calculate premiums. They spread the risk and the costs are shared. If United States health plans enrolled only premature babies, monthly premiums for each baby would have to be huge — tens of thousands of dollars. That would make health insurance completely unaffordable. No one would or could buy it.

There were several issues about insurance availability that needed to be addressed by each of the Ugandan health care co-ops. Those issues are universal. Obviously, fewer people would buy health insurance early as financial protection if they could simply wait until they were really sick before paying any premiums. It's a pretty simple concept. It holds true in the United States, and it is equally true in Uganda.

Those universal actuarial factors about the need to spread risk would all be relevant, we knew, and had to be addressed by any program in Uganda that was set up to insure local co-op members. We had to make sure that the only enrollees in the local co-ops weren't the local HIV/AIDS patients. If that happened, the program would self-destruct financially in a matter of months. Possibly weeks. But, we also didn't want to set up a program that couldn't offer care to those who needed it. Selling coverage only to a small number of healthy people would have been a relatively worthless endeavor. So, we had to come up with an approach that enrolled a cross section of the population and created a financially viable and affordable insurance risk pool overall for each local health care co-op.

The good news is that American insurers have evolved dozens of very workable and effective techniques for helping the insurer build insurable risk pools. Some of those techniques, we discovered, transplanted very nicely to Uganda. You'll read about them later in this book.

8) Easy to Administer — We knew that the slender available health care cash flow in Uganda would not and could not support or sustain any significant administration expense. In the United States, the HealthPartners health plan always kept administrative costs at slightly less than 10 percent of premium. That number is very efficient. It's on the very low end for American health plans. We bragged about it, in fact. Most people in American health care know that HealthPartners always has one of the lowest administrative cost levels in the country. The plan actually had dropped that number as a percentage of premium every year for a decade — a goal set by the member-elected board of directors of our plan. With an average per member revenue of $150 a month in 1997, that 10 percent gave us slightly under $15 a month per member to pay claims, send out bills, answer the phone, file the required government reports, and generally administer the program.

In Uganda, with total health care expenditures running at roughly $1 per Ugandan per month, we calculated very quickly that an equivalent 10 percent administrative level would only give us a dime to work with each month. You can't do too much with 10 cents, we thought, even in Uganda. We certainly couldn't just transplant the American administrative model for that amount.

We knew we had to develop an extremely simple, even elegant, way of handling the essential, bare bones administrative tasks that simply needed to be done to run any health plan. We knew that we had to cut out all non-essential administrative tasks, and reduce overhead and operational burdens down to the absolute bare minimum — to rock bottom — if we wanted the program to succeed. Our overall goal in Uganda was to stringently reduce costs, not add on a new insurance administrative burden that would, in the end, increase costs.

At most, we believed, the administrative costs necessary to run the program should not exceed half of whatever care-discount savings we managed to negotiate with local caregivers on behalf of local patients. So, we decided to try to do the job for a dime.

A dime is a tough target. Even, we would say, a sobering target. It inspired creativity. You'll read later about the steps we took to keep administrative costs at rock bottom levels.

9) An Approach People Would Trust — We set a goal of having a plan that was open, on-the-table, transparent, credible, trustworthy, and trusted. We knew from the stories they told us that many rural Ugandans had been deceived and defrauded multiple times by various parties purporting to be their friends and allies. We wanted our process to be both credible, and clearly deserving of credibility, from day one.

With those nine goals in mind, we set out to design a plan. That's when the fun began.

Chapter Three
Who Owns It? Who Runs It?

It's an old African tradition
of mutual self help.

$\mathcal{W}$e are co-op advocates. Those of us who helped start the Ugandan health care co-ops have long been strong advocates of consumer-owned, consumer-governed health care plans. The models of care delivery and financing we've helped design and implement in Uganda have been heavily influenced by that belief.

Each of the local Ugandan health care co-ops is self-governing. They are not subsidiary units of some larger controlling entity. Nor are they owned by any central, regional, national, or international health plan. Each local Uganda health care co-op runs its own plan, elects its own leadership, and selects its own care system partners.

Each local unit decides on its own benefit package and defines its own values, standards, and rules for issues like enrollment and underwriting. Examples of those decisions are listed later in this book. Amazingly complex insurance and coverage issues can be dealt with easily by the local co-op boards once the issues and relevant concepts have been clearly explained.

We believe that the cooperative model works well for health care. As I noted earlier, HealthPartners is a health care co-op, itself, in the United States, so the belief in that approach was more than theoretical. It's a very practical model we each worked with every day in our jobs. The HealthPartners team was all co-op people, so that's the approach we were committed to testing in Uganda.

Who Did We Work with First?

Starting a health care co-op in rural Africa is a fascinating process. In each community, we began by identifying likely prospects who might serve as the foundation for each local group. Existing dairy co-ops, for example, obviously make a great base for a health care co-op, for reasons that go beyond the fact that Land O'Lakes got us started in the first place with those particular co-ops.

Why are dairy co-ops easy to turn into health care co-ops?

The dairy co-ops are already organized. They have members. They have leaders. They have cash flow. They understand cooperative decision making. They already have a sense of the power, leverage, and effectiveness that can result from purchasing together and working together.

The dairy co-op leaders also have language and terminology that makes explaining a new health care co-op to their members relatively easy to do.

The dairy co-op members are also a self-selected group of non-passive people. They are action-oriented. The dairy co-op members have already begun very specific local group action to improve their economic lives, so they are more likely than some others to be both intellectually and emotionally inclined to take collective group action to also improve their health care.

Even though we started with dairy co-ops, we quickly learned that there were a number of other local Ugandan organizations that could be converted relatively easily to health care co-ops. Other types of agricultural co-ops were a logical and easy next step. There are several, relatively small, rural tea cooperatives in Uganda that offered very similar advantages when it came to forming health care co-ops. Also the tea co-ops were already organized, so calling an initial group meeting to discuss health care was a very doable event. They have effective in-place leaders. They need health care. Like the dairy co-op, the tea co-op members were already predisposed to working together toward a common goal. Two Ugandan tea co-ops have now formed their own micro health plans. One of the co-ops has even built its own local clinic using cooperative efforts and money.

Interestingly, we discovered that local micro credit groups that exist in some villages and towns come with similar advantages. The micro credit groups tend to be a lot smaller than the agricultural cooperatives, but there are very large numbers of them in some areas with very similar structures that can be an asset in the formation of micro health groups. The micro credit groups also elect their own leaders. They meet regularly, usually weekly, to discuss common issues. They already have measures in place for collecting and protecting cash.

Micro credit groups have achieved economic miracles in a

Meeting with dairy co-op leaders to describe the co-op.

number of developing countries. Uganda has been a leader in setting those groups up. Those groups have helped a lot of poor people become financially self-sufficient. It's a wonderful model that deserves widespread support. I'm currently on the Ambassadors Council of Freedom From Hunger, an organization set up to foster those kinds of programs in a dozen developing countries, because I believe so strongly in that approach. I was asked to serve on that Council in part as a result of my learnings about working with micro credit groups in Uganda. In any case, certain micro credit groups may well be another nice catalyst for forming health plans in some areas of the world.

Local "friendship" societies also exist in some settings in several African countries, including Uganda. I have also come across very similar "friendship societies" in southern parts of Africa. These societies are composed of people who literally get together as a very local society to help each other. It's an old African tradition of mutual (self) help. These "friendship" societies can also be the foundation for local health plans in some settings.

Quite a few communities in Africa also have strong local burial societies. Called Engozi Societies in Uganda, the burial societies form to help people, in effect, prepay for their own funerals. They organize funerals for members. Society members pay a small premium each month to receive the burial benefit when needed. Those burial societies can also, we found, become the core of small, local co-op health plans. One of the first health plans we worked with in Uganda has an Engozi Society as its core organization.

Who Decides What?

In the model we advocate, we start with a foundational organization — a dairy co-op, micro credit group, friendship society, or burial society. That foundational organization begins by getting its leadership together to study the issue carefully. Our staff helps the organization understand and discuss issues. The leadership then ultimately makes a formal decision as a group whether or not to become a health care co-op. Usually, after extensive conversations and discussions with all group members, a meeting is held in front of the entire group, and a vote is taken in a formal way about whether or not to become a health care co-op. Our Ugandan staff helps the group members think that decision through. It doesn't happen overnight. A series of meetings are held. Our staff helps the group leaders and members understand the various financial issues involved, talks through the local care system selection issues, and ultimately helps survey all group members to check out the likely level of support and participation for a health care co-op. It is extremely important for the group leadership and the group members to understand exactly what is involved in becoming a health care co-op. That can take some long, thorough, and occasionally heated conversations.

If all of those discussions result in a positive decision by the burial society, or the credit group, or the tea co-op to go forward as a health care co-op, that merely starts the overall decision-making process for the group. The foundational entity then has to make a series of very specific operational, organizational, and coverage decisions as a group. At that point, the group begins the process of establishing its own rules and functional guidelines. That decision-making process needs to be carefully constructed and supported for best results. That's the job of our Ugandan staff — to support and structure that process of local group decision-making.

The next chapter describes the specific underwriting decisions that have to be made by each co-op. The following chapters describe the benefit decisions. Each local group also decides very early in the process which local caregivers they would like to use for their care. When the first set of decisions has been made, and the co-op has elected its leaders, then serious negotiations can begin with the local caregivers.

HealthPartners has trained local Ugandan staff members from the Uganda Health Cooperatives to directly facilitate all of the discussions that result in each of those group decisions. That facilitation role is further described in Chapter Eight.

Each local co-op, itself, then owns and fully understands the resulting local health plan. That ownership is generally very empowering to the co-op members. In a couple of cases, as I noted earlier, empowered and motivated local co-ops have actually chosen to build small clinics directly. That's a model we know well, since the HealthPartners co-op in the United States owns two dozen clinics and directly employs hundreds of physicians. HealthPartners also contracts with several thousand additional physicians to make sure that all of the plan's American members have easy and convenient access to care. The Ugandan health cooperatives have each made very similar "make/buy" decisions relative to care. In most cases, the co-ops simply serve as purchasing groups and buy care and coverage from local-contracted caregivers. In some cases, as noted above, the co-ops are actually building clinics. In one case, a tea co-op has now constructed a tiny hospital. Without that hospital, the nearest care would be 35 kilometers away, too far to go with a broken leg or for a pregnant woman in labor.

The Goal Is Self-Sustaining Care Co-Ops

One of the reasons we believe so strongly in the local governance model and the local decision-making process is that a major goal of ours was to have the Ugandan units be self-sustaining — capable of surviving our departure as an ally and organizing force. We didn't want to start a centralized, bureaucratic, essentially commercial, and externally controlled model that was dependent on our continued presence to be able to negotiate renewed contracts with their local caregivers or to make decisions about key operational issues.

To that end, a major objective has been to give each of the local co-ops all of the intellectual and operational skills, tools, and concepts they need to be self-sustaining. That education process is closely tied to the rigid strategy we used: all staff in Uganda must be native Ugandans, trained to set up and run local health plans, rather than having a set of visiting Americans temporarily managing a local care system they are each planning to leave.

That model of having American managers run local plans can probably work in many settings. But in Uganda, we wanted to err on the side of local sustainability. We put together a really strong local staff. Building that strong local staff was a key strategic goal. The local staff has been trained to help each local co-op get organized and operational. An equally important part of the strategy has been to teach each of the local co-ops the key tools they need to run and renew co-ops with little or no external help. As the old adage goes, we didn't want to give them fish — we wanted to teach them how to fish. The decision-making process used to set up each local co-op was a key piece of teaching them how to fish.

Let's Get Maximum Mileage for the Process

As noted earlier, even though HealthPartners has provided the systems, training, and support necessary to start local health plans for the co-op and micro health plan members, we have not, at any level, wanted to restrict the ability of the local prepaid providers in any community to reach out in a similar way to other local patients. HealthPartners facilitated a strong program that reaches out to nearly 10,000 school children from one Ugandan hospital. The school children are all in local Bushenyi schools. Before the prepaid program existed, most of those children were without medical care. Some literally died of malaria in their dorm beds, far from home and far from enough money to seek care. Schools had, at best, access to a school nurse. Now the students in those schools have prepaid coverage and a solid local medical group that manages both their care and their health.

We also facilitated the extension of a local tea grower co-op plan tied to a local tea factory — with more than 800 members joining a local hospital plan based on the tea plan. In those situations and cases, the health plan of record is the local caregiver, not a Uganda Health Cooperative. We believe the core Uganda Health Cooperative plan and initiative is strengthened as a result of those programs, not weakened. The likelihood of care being available for the members of our co-ops is enhanced, not diminished, when the caregivers can also build other prepaid approaches to serve other local patients.

At some future time, there may be issues for concern. The new care-system-run health plans could become plan and provider monopolies for their regions, and they could raise prices accordingly. That doesn't concern HealthPartners because the immediate care needs of the local people are so great that those long-term possibilities aren't even relevant.

The first goal to achieve success for micro health co-ops is to have a local buying coalition — a health care co-op — with sufficient membership and credibility to get the providers' attention. The second need is to have a care system partner — a local care team that will work with the co-op on a prepaid basis to provide affordable and needed care.

If those pieces come together well, great synergy can result. It can be done. We've seen it happen.

So, what decisions do these local health plans have to make? Quite a few. They are described in the next several chapters.

These are the exact same decisions, by the way, that major health plans and major purchasers of care need to make in America. The scale is different, but as you will see, the main issues of health care financing are pretty much universal.

Chapter Four
The Devil's In the Details

*Totally "free" care often tends to be
both undervalued and overused.*

*D*o not underestimate the ability of very local health care
co-ops to make very important decisions about the basic financial
and operational issues for their own local plan.

One of the most enjoyable and interesting days we had in
Uganda was spent in a small, electricity-free hut in the mountains.
Long-horned cattle, looking in through the open windows, listened
to a spirited and incredibly sophisticated debate about the appropriate level and role of maternity coverage. For the nearly formed
local health care co-op, the underlying issue was the cost of the
premium. To keep the premium costs down, one side argued that
only catastrophic maternity care should be covered by the local
plan. Normal deliveries, that side argued, are predictable, affordable,
and budgetable events, not "insurable" events. They argued that the
plan should not cover normal childbirth in the benefit package.

"Anyone who knows she is pregnant has at least seven months
to save money for the doctor or midwife," one man argued.
"Insurance should be for things we can't expect, and for expenses
we can't anticipate. C-sections are different. If you need an
unexpected operation to deliver a baby, then the plan should pay.

Otherwise, for normal deliveries you should each budget. Responsible people plan ahead and budget for these things. I don't want my monthly payment to be used to pay for other people's normal maternity costs."

Others in the room disagreed.

"I don't plan to get pregnant," one woman said. "It just happens. I can't budget for it because I have no money. I need the health plan to have the delivery benefit, or I won't be able to hire a doctor or nurse for my delivery."

Another man said, "My wife can't have any more children. She's too old. Why should I pay a higher premium to pay for your baby? No one paid for any of mine. You should pay for your own babies."

Yet another voice said, "If we don't have the benefit, my wife won't be able to see the doctor before the baby is born. If there's a problem at the birth, maybe that's too late. It would have been better to have the doctor see her earlier. But, we don't have the money to pay for those visits."

The debate went on for a couple of hours. Outside the window, we could see a couple of tall, skinny boys with long straight shepherds' staffs herding a dozen of those magnificent Ugandan cows. Ugandan cattle have been bred for centuries for the size of their horns. Many Ugandan cattle have horns that make Texas Longhorns look like Minnesota Shorthorns.

Land O'Lakes has been importing cattle semen into Uganda for the dairy cooperatives to upgrade the milk production levels of the local cattle. The result is sometimes visually staggering. You can see black and white cattle with six-foot horn spreads, looking like Wisconsin dairy cows on major steroids. One of those strangely out-of-proportion cows was obviously enjoying the maternity coverage debate, poking her nose into the open window periodically to hear the next point being made. Only her nose fit into the room. Her horns reached well past the window on both sides.

Ugandan cows

In the end, after extensive and sometimes mildly heated debate, that particular local health plan decision-making council decided not to cover normal maternity for the first year, but to negotiate it into their contract with the local physician provider and hospital in year two or three.

Cesarean sections and other complications of pregnancy were, however, covered by that health plan for both the mother and the child in year one. The winning argument was that no one plans for a C-section, so it should be an insured event.

Most Ugandan co-op sites have decided to cover full maternity care after year one — but generally each new mother has to be enrolled in the plan for a full year before her pregnancy is covered. The issue of "anti-selection" is readily understood by small groups of consumers whose personal money is paying the premiums. When your own shillings are in the payment pot, you don't look kindly on someone who doesn't ante up her monthly premium until she knows she is already pregnant.

One of the ways that HealthPartners has brought value to the small health plans of Uganda was to frame the discussion and debate on each of the major "underwriting rule" issues that need to be resolved for each co-op. We brought in the usual American health insurance actuarial and underwriting toolkit and clearly presented the available options to the local co-ops. The co-op board in each village makes its own decisions about which actuarial rules or options to choose.

Providing Care To Our Members

Once the basic underwriting and benefit choices are made, we then go to the local care system to negotiate the price for providing care to our members. In the first rounds, those provider negotiations were typically done by HealthPartners staff — American and Ugandan — on behalf of the local co-op. More recently, the Ugandan staff has been handling the whole process. Renewals are done between the local co-op leaders and the local providers of care, with the HealthPartners Ugandan staff available to advise and assist when asked or as needed.

Provider contracting involves a set of teachable skills. After year one, the local co-op worked with our Ugandan staff to do the provider contract renewals. The Minnesotans tended to be out of the loop at that point, except as readily available advisors. The internet has been a great connectivity tool between the HealthPartners staff in Minnesota and the Ugandans who run the program in that country.

Sample contracts and underwriting standards are available, by the way, from HealthPartners. Again, simply using United States contracts was not a workable approach. Ugandan contracts needed some very specific Ugandan features. It was particularly interesting to note, for example, the variations in the definition of "family" in each local contract. Some families had multiple wives. Others included one or more grandparents. Some included adopted children. In each case, the local co-op had to decide who was eligible for coverage under the definition of "family." Those were all obviously local decisions.

Fairness

A major goal of the local co-op benefit and actuarial discussions is always fairness. How do we fairly and equitably cover the most people without opening the door to a negative situation where only sick people join the plan, and the plan itself dies financially under that cost burden?

Those very same risk pool composition issues have been dealt with many times in the United States, so we were able to offer a menu of American insurance approaches for consideration by the Ugandan co-ops. In some regards, insurance issues are insurance issues — wherever you are.

So, what specific issues are on the template of insurance policy options for decision making by the local Ugandan co-op leaders? The usual set — eligibility issues, underwriting rules and techniques, benefit design, and payer liability issues always lead the list. Each of those issues has to be framed in a way that allows the local co-op leaders to understand the concepts, weigh the choices, and make decisions in the best interest of their fellow co-op members.

We ask each local co-op to decide whether or not to use enrollment windows, quotas, pre-existing condition exclusions, riders, co-payments, in-network care exclusivity, and coordination of benefits. If you are not an insurance expert, that last sentence may have seemed like gobbledygook, or least, excessive jargon. But each term represents a basic and simple concept that lends itself to local decision making. We needed to explain each of those tools to the local co-op, and then we needed to facilitate a very well-informed local debate about whether or not to use them in each setting. The tools really aren't that complicated once the basic concepts are understood. You'll get some sense of that from the examples below.

Enrollment Windows

As noted in the last chapter, one tool that can work to protect the financial viability of the co-op is to ensure that people don't wait until they are sick before joining the plan. One way of doing that is to require people in the founding group to either enroll in the health plan within a specified timeframe or not be eligible to join. Our experience is that the local co-op members really do understand and support the practical essence and value of this time-limited enrollment issue when it is explained clearly to them. Since the co-ops do not want people joining them only after they are sick and in terrible need of care, one enrollment rule that can be used by a local co-op is to say, "In this village, only people who join before April of this year will be allowed into the plan this year. Everyone else will have to wait for next April to join."

That approach resembles one that has been widely used in the United States. Most health plans and employer groups in the United States traditionally have annual open enrollment periods, rather than allowing people to just join when their health fails.

An alternative version of that approach used by some Ugandan co-ops has been to say that only the people who join before a given date will have full coverage. Anyone who joins after that date will have limited coverage — with no coverage for one year for certain conditions like HIV/AIDS, pregnancy, diabetes, and a selected list of diseases. Again, the goal is to get healthy people in the risk pool early so that the total premium is sufficient to pay for needed care. Setting enrollment timeframes is a good and workable tool that helps local co-ops protect their risk pool, because people need to decide whether or not to join at a time when they aren't sick. Each co-op decides what enrollment windows make sense for their own members. That rule sometimes changed in later years of operation.

Quotas

Quotas, as noted earlier, are also a topic that local co-op members generally spend time resolving with great practicality and wisdom. Quotas are a predetermined percentage of the original group (a dairy co-op for example) who have to join the health care co-op before the plan begins operations. If the health care co-op start-up plan states, "We won't start this health plan until 60 percent of the original tea co-op members sign-up," then there is a very strong incentive for all of the true believers in the tea group to work hard to enroll sufficient numbers of people to get the plan started. Sixty percent was a number we calculated based on an assessment of the risk factors in a typical co-op group. It's not pure science, nor is it a magic number. But, it seems to work. When 60 percent have joined, the odds are much better that the actual enrolled risk pool is somewhat representative of the overall community health and not skewed entirely toward the very ill. Every health plan in Uganda has used initial enrollment quotas to get the plan started. Sixty percent is usually the target.

In very practical terms, if a typical dairy co-op has 50 families, 30 families must both sign-up for the program and pay their premium before the program is operational. That isn't always easy to achieve. Someone has to actually enroll the 60 percent — usually in face-to-face conversations with many of the people. Who does that work? Typically, it's the local co-op leaders. It's hard work.

The co-op leaders often must go from home to home, enrolling families one at a time, until those 30 families come on board. That initial enrollment process can sometimes take a couple of months. It takes time, but it's an important first step, and the enrollment process itself creates an internal group momentum that can be helpful in other areas.

Again, quotas are not a hard approach to explain. People understand the need. To repeat myself, the basic concept of each health co-op is that enough healthy families must be enrolled for the total premium collected to offset the costs of care for the sickest people and the sickest families. Local care providers understand that particular issue very well. Our experience has been that the local providers who contract with each co-op feel very comfortable with a rigidly enforced quota rule. The actuarial need is pretty clear to the providers. Most local providers actually would not contract with the co-op for any prepaid care if that rule wasn't in place.

Co-op members also generally understand the issues and concerns involved and feel that the concept of a quota is a fair and reasonable negotiating issue for the care providers. We haven't seen any resentment toward quotas on the part of co-op leaders who have the sometimes challenging task of achieving those quotas.

To date, the 60 percent quota number seems to be a good one. At 60 percent, enough healthy families join the co-op to make up for the sicker members. When the enrollment percentage numbers go past 60, the risk pool often gets even better.

In the United States, insurers use similar rules for setting up new groups and renewing old ones. In those instances where American employers make participation in a health plan a voluntary decision for employees, insurers generally require an 80 percent or higher participation level within an employer group. As a rule, if more than 20 percent of the employees in a small company refuse to be part of the employer's health plan, in many states American insurers can and will cancel coverage for the entire group. The risk pool deterioration issues are the same in both countries. The United States insurers know that for any given group of insured employees, roughly 20 percent of the group will have no claims at all — and 5 percent of the group will have more than 50 percent of the claims. The premium from the non-users is needed or else the rates would have to be a lot higher for the few sick people who do join the plan.

Is 60 percent the right number? It seems to be. In Uganda, we now believe that it might even be possible to go to a 50 percent number, based on the utilization data from the first co-ops. It may be that the 60 percent number is needed for first enrollment, but 50 percent would be enough to renew the group. The analysis is underway.

In any case, each local co-op has to decide whether or not to use a quota number — and, if one is used, then the co-op has to decide on a quota percentage. If the co-op decides not to use a quota, then getting local caregivers to agree to a prepaid "risk" contract would generally be a lot harder.

Picking the right percentage is a major decision. As noted above, if the percentage is too low, the providers can be unhappy — and possibly unwilling to participate as a prepaid partner to the plan. If the number is set at a very safe 80 percent or higher, then it can be extremely difficult — if not impossible — to get a sufficient enrollment percentage to activate the plan. A quota of 80 percent would probably be hopeless in most cases. Incomes in Uganda are very low. At any given point in time, more than 20 percent of any given rural Uganda group is unable or unwilling to pay any premium at all.

The reason that quotas work to help create a viable risk pool is because the original group of people come together for a reason other than buying health insurance. So, the distribution of sick and healthy people in those groups is likely to be financially workable. Very well-proven actuarial theory tells us that quotas work best when the original groups were each formed for some purpose other than buying health insurance. Because health wasn't their organizing factor, those non-health groups in their entirety are likely to represent a reasonable spread of local health risk. It's a good thing, actuarially, when the specific relevant groups were formed to grow and sell tea, for example, or to help members buy fruit stands. The starting point for that group's health care risk pool is, therefore, not a group of sick people who have self-selected into a purchasing organization purely for reasons of buying health care, or health insurance.

If, on the other hand, the starting point for forming any health plan would be to assemble a group of people who all have health problems, the quota approach would, by definition, not work. That seems breathtakingly obvious, but even in the United States, some people don't understand that basic principle. Some people believe that "pooling" — all by itself — somehow in some magic way cuts insurance costs. Wrong. The total cost of care for 20 cancer patients doesn't go down just because those 20 sick people form a group and buy insurance together. If a group of homeowners whose houses are already burning down form a fire insurance buying group, that doesn't help make their fire insurance affordable. Pooling alone isn't the key. Getting together in a risk pool that isn't disproportionately sick is the key.

Therefore, quotas and pooling usually work best if the core purchasing group was initially started for some other reason.

Health-Based Individual Enrollment Rejections

Another technique that is widely used in the United States by insurers to protect and improve the health status of the risk pools they insure is to use a "health screen" and an individual health examination to determine who is or is not covered. Both individual health insurance and life insurance companies use those kinds of screening techniques regularly. In the most candid description, the goal of the insurer in doing the screening is to detect unhealthy people before they are covered, and then refuse to sell them coverage. Life insurance companies tend not to issue coverage to people who have had several heart attacks or who currently suffer from cancer, for example.

Health insurers do the same in some small portions of the United States health insurance marketplace. It is illegal in the United States to discriminate, to reject, or to cancel coverage for people with group insurance. Those laws are pretty clear. Non-group or "individual" health insurance is a different matter. If individual Americans who don't have "group" coverage through their employer attempt to purchase individual health insurance, in almost all cases, the insurance company will require each individual applicant for coverage to fill out a health history form. Sometimes, an actual health exam is required. The goal is to avoid covering only sick and expensive people in the individual insurance risk pool for each insurer. In Uganda, it would theoretically be possible to use that same health screening technique. A local co-op could theoretically screen the health status of each applicant and prevent anyone with diabetes or heart disease or HIV/AIDS from enrolling.

That approach, at least slightly, contradicts some of the basic underlying values of the cooperative group purchasing approach, because it inherently denies care to some of the members of the group who need it.

It would also make sales very difficult in Uganda because a high percentage of families have HIV/AIDS. Rejecting every family with an HIV-positive person would cut the market by more than half in some areas of the country.

But, even if that problem didn't exist, using individual health screening involving looking at each applicant's personal health status would still not work in the co-ops in Uganda. It's too expensive. From a pure logistical perspective, it would be extremely expensive in Uganda to attempt to do actual physical examinations for each applicant for coverage. There's simply not enough money in the premium to pay for these screening exams. How much premium would be needed from a family of eight people to pay for giving each of them full pre-enrollment physical exams? In a nation with extremely scarce caregiver resources, what physician or nurse would even be available to give those eight "insurance" exams?

The good news is that full health screening of all individuals is not needed by the co-ops if the quota rules do the job.

To date, no Ugandan health care co-op has chosen to use a formal, pre-enrollment individual health screen of each applicant to determine who can or cannot enroll. But, the issue is usually debated and it might well be used at some point in some more densely populated urban settings as more caregivers are available, more medical information is known about individuals, and the quota system is less effective because the founding group is not a co-op founded for other purposes.

Pre-Existing Condition Exclusions

Another risk pool protection technique that the co-op leaders tend to clearly and quickly understand is the "pre-ex" or pre-existing condition exclusion. A "pre-ex" means that a person is not covered for a pre-existing health problem. To save money and avoid anti-selection in selling coverage, some insurers in the United States say that a newly insured person is fully covered immediately for all "new" diseases, but isn't covered at all for any negative health conditions that already exist on or before the individual's date of enrollment. That concept and logic is easy to explain and work with for the Ugandan co-op leaders. Some very good, in-depth discussions have been held on that topic — with some variations being made between co-ops in the final decision making about which health conditions, if any, should be subjected to a pre-existing condition exclusion or benefit reduction.

Pregnancy is one of the most common conditions affected by a pre-ex exclusion. Often, a new pregnancy would be covered but a pregnancy already in process would be excluded from coverage for a new member. In that case — in part to avoid what used to be a constant and unwinnable battle about whether a nine-month pre-ex could be fairly applied to an eight-month baby — some American insurers have moved to flat two-year pre-ex exclusion periods for maternity coverage. Biology is, in part, the inspiration for that number. No woman carries a baby for twenty-four months. And, if the baby is born in 23 or even 24 months, it usually doesn't happen often enough to be worth the claims denial fight for the insurer.

In Uganda, several local plans have had great debates on these topics and have set up definite pre-ex exclusion periods — particularly for pregnancy and HIV/AIDS.

The decision-making discussions on those topics have also been well worth hearing. Usually, the maternity pre-ex is set at one year. Ugandan women give birth far too often for a two-year pre-ex to be seen as adding value.

Riders

A variation of the pre-ex is what we Americans call the "rider." (No one seems to know exactly why this provision is called a rider. Perhaps it "rides" on top of the normal member contract?)

"Riders" are amendments to an individual member's contract that permanently exclude benefits for a particular and specific health condition. An American patient who wants to buy individual insurance and who has had heart surgery, for example, might find that the insurance carrier would cover him for every other health care issue or problem, but will exclude coverage for any future heart surgeries. A "heart rider" would be added to that person's contract. Cancer would still be covered for that person, for example, but an open-heart surgery would not.

Damaged hips and knees are often "ridered" out of individual contracts in the United States.

A person with a knee "rider" based on a prior knee injury could re-injure that knee and treatment would not be insured. Again, the goal of the insurer is to avoid people buying insurance coverage only because their knee is once again damaged, and they know they now need a $10,000 knee surgery. At that point, with no rider, if each injured person could simply pay a $200 monthly premium, and in the process actually buy $10,000 worth of knee care, that would be a great deal for the new member, but an unfair financial expense for the insurer.

In the United States "riders" are now illegal in almost all

official and regulated group insurance and HMO contracts. They also don't exist in government programs. They are used only by those carriers that sell individual coverage. They can be found in that particular marketplace, however.

Using riders in Uganda has its drawbacks. Riders actually are not an easy or convenient thing to do anywhere. "Riders" are typically a real pain to administer. They are a challenge for the insurer to even remember — year to year. It's hard to tell who has a "rider." Doctors who don't know about the rider might treat a seemingly fully insured patient — expecting the plan to provide coverage — only to discover that particular "ridered" condition and treatment has to be billed directly to the patient.

Very few of the Uganda sites have elected to use "riders." The ones that have used riders only for pre-diagnosed cases of HIV/AIDS. (Undiagnosed cases of HIV/AIDS are always covered — to the extent that local caregivers can directly provide local care).

Again, the local co-op boards have engaged in spirited discussions about the use of both pre-ex and riders — with different sites reaching different conclusions.

Co-payments

Another risk management/utilization control tool that American insurance companies use is co-payments. Co-payments manage risk in a very different way. Instead of preventing sick people from joining the plan, co-payments are intended to keep relatively well people from overusing the plan.

Totally free care often tends to be both undervalued and overused. That is equally true in the United States and in Africa. Knowing that to be an issue, each of the local Ugandan co-ops has set up per-visit co-payments for patient care. The co-payments typically run at 900 shillings per visit, or 50 cents in United States currency. On some sites, the co-payment for a day in the hospital is slightly more than the co-payment for a clinic visit. Each time the patient visits a clinic, the co-payment is collected by the clinic itself. The plan is not involved in either billing or collection.

The co-pays both discourage unneeded doctor visits and give the hospitals and clinics a nice ancillary cash flow, in addition to the premium payment, to help offset some variable costs of clinical operation. Since the co-pays are generally low enough to be affordable, they tend to be actually paid by the patient, rather than turning into uncollectible bad debt for the doctor.

The local co-op leadership, generally, in consultation with the local hospital and doctors, also sets the co-pay levels for each type of care. If you looked at sample HealthPartners of Uganda contracts you would see that different co-op sites have selected different co-pay levels. Every co-op plan in Uganda uses some version of co-payments.

Co-payments can also be used in some creative ways to influence care in a positive way.

A Ugandan co-op — to encourage women to seek prenatal care — eliminates the hospital delivery co-payment if the mother has had two prenatal visits. Another site, trying also to incent the same good health status, uses a penalty instead of a reward and refuses to pay for the delivery altogether unless the mother has had two or more prenatal visits.

It's possible to be very creative with co-payments. If they become too complex, however, it becomes harder to explain the plan and harder to make new sales.

Local Care Only

A major benefit limitation in Uganda that actually plays a major role in keeping the local co-op plans from insolvency is the fact that each local health co-op only provides the care that is available from local participating providers. "Out-of-area" care is simply and clearly not covered. That is an economic necessity for the Ugandan care co-ops. When the premium runs at a very low level to be affordable, it is impossible to provide full insurance for all needed local care and then also cover, through the same insurance funding, the expenses of out-of-area care — care provided by physicians and hospitals that are not under contract to the local co-op.

There has been some talk of creating a specialty referral network in Uganda that links the rural hospitals to the big multi-specialty hospitals in the capital city of Kampala. The Kampala hospitals offer many more services. But, a sad fact of life is that a premium of only 10,000 shillings a quarter for a family of four equals about $6. You can't buy very much specialty care for $6. Even in Kampala.

Even if you could, every penny of that tiny premium is already spent and overspent on local care. There simply isn't any money available from the Bushenyi premium to pay for a neuro-surgeon at Nsambya. So, only local care is covered.

The contracts for each local co-op very clearly limit coverage to care that can be provided at the local hospital or by the local providers.

By American standards, that's a pretty limited benefit set. By Ugandan standards, however, that's a lot better than no care at all. A lot better. It covers malaria, dysentery, parasitic infections, and 90 percent of the local care needs of most Ugandans.

Benefit Maximums

A related tool for expense limitations that can be used by the local co-ops is to decide to have a maximum benefit level set.

Benefit maximums are limits in the amount of local care that a local co-op will pay for a given patient. Again, that makes eco-nomic sense. Plans with very finite amounts of money can't pay for infinite amounts of care. Even for very local care, a few benefit limits and benefit maximums had to be established in most co-op sites to keep the providers from insolvency. So how are the benefits capped? Benefits can be capped by counting services or by setting a maximum cost. Benefit caps that are used include approaches like limiting patients to 30 days of hospital care each year for some co-ops, or limiting coverage to 100,000 shillings worth of hospital care for others.

Those limitations are generally well accepted in the local communities because even that somewhat limited benefit set provides an enormous service to the plan members — a service that was unavailable to many people before each local plan was started. Very few patients exceed those benefit caps.

At some future time, an expansion of services to "out-of-area" care would be desirable. But the amount of money involved will be a major challenge. And the impact on local caregiving would need to be carefully considered.

A key to the success of each local program is the willingness of local caregivers to accept prepayment risk arrangements. Without local providers, these co-ops cannot exist. Having local providers sign contracts is an essential piece of the entire co-op package. If the benefits that the provider must deliver are unlimited, then the potential financial risk for the care providers is also unlimited. That's too much risk for many small hospitals and local providers to take on. So the co-op benefits need to have maximum levels in certain areas to manage the providers' risk levels. The challenge, of course, is to have the benefits complete enough to meet the needs of most patients but not so rich that they potentially bankrupt the at-risk providers.

Again, each site has carefully reached its own conclusions on these matters. Practicality was the key decision factor in each case.

Coordination of Benefits

One other cost-limiting American insurance practice that was transplanted to Uganda was a surprise to us. Coordination of benefits (COB) is a process used in the United States to determine which insurer pays for care when a patient is covered by more than one health plan or insurer. The rules of COB have been carefully negotiated in the United States between all major insurers — to the point where multiple coverage situations are handled easily in almost all cases. If someone is insured by two or more American health insurers, there are very clear rules about how much each carrier must pay for the patient's care. Double payments do not occur. (Before COB, some people deliberately bought duplicate insurance plans in the United States and then made a lot of money by receiving a lot of care.)

We didn't expect COB to be an issue in Uganda because there really isn't any other private health insurance in the country. A Kenyan company called African Air Rescue (AAR) owns a couple of Ugandan clinics and keeps a couple of fixed-wing air ambulances at the Kampala airport. AAR sells a form of partial "health insurance" to a small market of upper income Ugandans. The AAR benefit package consists both of local care provided through their own clinics and in getting truly sick and well-to-do people into those small airplanes and out of the country when needed. European hospitals are a preferred destination for most AAR enrollees. Some go to South Africa.

Other than that, our tiny coalition of local health plans was now just about the only form of health insurance available in the country. So, we didn't initially think the COB tool needed to be lifted out of the American insurance toolkit.

HIV/AIDS and immunizations caused us to think otherwise. The government has limited HIV/AIDS treatment programs available in a couple of large regional hospitals. Since our local doctors and hospitals had no real access to HIV/AIDS drugs or to the most current HIV/AIDS treatment programs, most sites put a COB clause in the member contract making the government "primary" on any available HIV/AIDS treatments. "Primary," in COB language, means "they pay first."

There were two reasons for that provision. We didn't want the government rejecting our HIV/AIDS patients because "they already have insurance coverage." We also didn't want the government sending bills to the local co-ops demanding payment for HIV/AIDS treatment and care available for free to all other Ugandans. We didn't want to inadvertently handicap our members in any way relative to access to HIV/AIDS care.

The government has been absolutely supportive of these health care co-ops in every way. We had great government cooperation and a high level of enthusiasm. We had no fear that the government would deliberately do anything to hurt these little plans. But, we thought some regional hospital financial manager might start sending out bills, and we didn't want our members to find themselves in that situation.

Likewise, on immunizations, each local plan covers and strongly encourages immunizations. The government periodically makes vaccines available for free. That is a wonderful thing. When we can get free vaccines, we use them. We wrote the COB clause making the government "primary" on immunizations so no local official could decide to cut off the supply of those vaccines to the co-op's children or charge the co-op for them.

Who, Exactly, Is a Family?

As noted earlier, one other actuarial issue that needed resolution in each site was the definition of "family." That issue was closely related to a decision about the premium levels to be charged for family coverage. It's an issue that may seem uniquely Ugandan, but it does have its parallel situation in American health care.

The questions to be answered about families in Uganda were these:

1) Who exactly is defined to be in the family?
2) If there is more than one wife, do we charge a second premium for each additional wife and her children?
3) Family sizes vary widely. Should there be just one family premium regardless of family composition, or should the

basic family premium cover a specified number of people with any additional people costing additional premium?

Again, various co-op sites answered those questions differently, each with its own sense of fairness, wisdom, and local culture.

My own favorite underwriting definition of a family came from a very rural co-op who said, "A family is a group of people who sleep under one roof and eat from one pot."

In that village, for that community, that was the perfect definition. It was their answer. It works. It's in the contract. The people who run that co-op know exactly how to interpret and enforce that rule. The group is small enough so that everyone actually knows who sleeps under that roof.

In other sites, families were defined as the husband, first wife, and their children. Generally, an additional premium was required for additional wives. The additional premium was usually a bit lower than the original "family" rate, however, because the husband's cost was already covered on the first premium. And, the second family was often smaller.

The general pattern was to define a family as a husband, wife, and up to five kids. That was covered by the basic premium. An additional premium was charged for each additional child. A whole new premium was required for each additional wife and her children.

Most local plans did set a size limit for family coverage. To avoid the obvious "risk selection" problem that could occur if a family enrolled only their sick kids, the usual required quota for enrollment in each family is 100 percent of the family members related to each wife. You can't just buy coverage for five of your seven or 11 kids. Otherwise, a large and complex family could pay just the basic premium, and then, selectively enroll only their sickest children from each wife in the plan. That's against the rules. You can, however, in most co-ops usually buy coverage for only one wife.

We had to do some careful contract writing at one point

when we discovered that the "family" is legally defined in Uganda as "a man and his children." The wife is not clearly defined as a member of the family in some legal lights — so we needed to be very specific in including the wives in the definition of family to be sure that they were, in fact, covered.

One of our favorite co-ops, the Women's Co-Op of Kirinya, is comprised entirely of women. The majority of the women are widows. Land O'Lakes set up the co-op to help women—many of whom were war widows or HIV/AIDS widows — get a fair price for the milk from their cows. The dairy co-op has been a major asset to the women — keeping them from being cheated in the sale of their milk.

In that setting, almost all of those families have no adult male in the home, so our family contract has a version that speaks to "a woman and her family."

HIV/AIDS has devastated much of Uganda. It had an unexpected and terrible impact on families as an unintended consequence of an old Ugandan custom that has, for centuries, protected the families. The custom has been that when a man dies, his children immediately become his brother's children, and his wife or wives become his brother's wife or wives.

That approach kept families strong and intact in past generations. There wasn't even a word in the tribal language for "orphan" because it wasn't needed. Due to large families, there was almost always a surviving brother or uncle, so Ugandan kids always had a dad.

HIV/AIDS, however, turned that custom of caring into a cycle of dying. Why? It's basic biology. The odds are high that when a man dies of HIV/AIDS, his surviving wife also has HIV/AIDS. If that wife automatically then becomes his surviving brother's wife, the HIV/AIDS virus moves to a new family and takes root. The new husband generally gets the virus. If that new husband dies before all of his wives are dead, the set of surviving wives from that husband goes on to the next brother — and then to the uncles.

A nation that didn't even have a word for orphan now has at least 1.5 million HIV/AIDS orphans. Widows are everywhere — many of them infected with the virus.

The government is doing everything it can to bring the virus under control — and there are some signs that the number of new cases is abating — but in some parts of the country a majority of the women giving birth in the hospitals now test HIV-positive.

This isn't an issue that will be resolved soon. It definitely makes starting health plans a challenge. And a necessity.

Making the Decisions Can Take Time

The entire process of each new co-op making decisions about quotas, benefit restrictions, enrollment periods, and definitions of what is considered to be a "family" can take a couple of months. That entire decision-making process also serves to educate the local decision makers, because they participate so completely in the process. They learn, in effect, by doing — and the learning helps create an intellectual framework that, hopefully, will help the local co-ops survive and renew themselves over time.

A key training process involved teaching these tools and concepts to the Ugandan staff so well that the staff could, in turn, teach them the co-ops. That process has gone well — and seems to be self-sustaining in most settings.

Chapter Five
Hitting Our 10-Cent Target

In a paperless culture, the ID cards are the only family
photographs that most of the members have ever had.

$\mathcal{A}$s I noted earlier, health care costs in Uganda run slightly over $12 per person per year. That includes all money spent on health by the government, charities, and private partners. Our initial market assessment, from meeting with the dairy co-op members, told us that the maximum affordable premium that could be paid by most rural co-op members would be about $1 per member, per month. If the premium was any higher, very few people could afford to join the co-op. So the challenge we faced as planners was to figure out how to live within the constraints of those numbers.

As we looked at setting up health care programs in Uganda, those numbers told us pretty clearly and very quickly that there was very little money available for care and a lot less available for administration.

We started by making an assumption about how much money could and should be diverted from premium to pay for administrative expenses. We decided to begin with a 10 percent goal. Why 10 percent?

As I noted earlier, we set 10 percent as our goal for two reasons. One is that we ran our own health plan in the United

States for about 10 percent. The other is that we didn't believe that much more than 10 percent could be diverted from the meager stream of available revenue and still buy enough needed care from local caregivers.

That created an interesting challenge. If we set a 10 percent administrative load target for the health care co-ops, and charged roughly $1 per month in premium, that left us with slightly less than a dime a month for non-care expenses.

In the United States, as I mentioned, the HealthPartners plan has one of the lowest administrative cost levels in the country — running below 10 percent — and it still cost us well over $15 per month per member in 1997 to administer our program. How does that money get spent? We spend our American administrative money to pay claims, issue ID cards, keep membership records, collect revenue, maintain eligibility files, negotiate with care providers, run sales campaigns, operate computers, and perform all of the other various and sundry operational tasks and accounting functions required of American insurers and businesses by law, regulation, structure, and custom. Many United States health plans spend upwards of 15 percent of revenue to perform those functions. Some spend more than 20 percent. So 10 percent is a good number.

Clearly, however, a dollar-for-dollar, piece-by-piece transplant of that entire, very expensive American administrative cost burden to Uganda would be crippling. The entire premium we were able to negotiate and collect from members in health co-ops in Uganda for total coverage couldn't begin to handle just our administrative overhead in the United States.

That fact presented a challenge. We had to figure out a way of creating an approach that was so simple and elegant that the administration of a Ugandan health plan could run on pennies and still run well.

As an added challenge, we needed to do that in a setting where most of our contracted care sites and all of our members had no hard-wired telephone connections and no in-place electronic communications infrastructure.

To succeed, we needed to strip plan expenses down to the absolute bare bones — to the most elegant and minimal level. We needed to eliminate all duplication of effort, avoid all expensive paperwork, and cut out all unnecessary administrative steps while somehow still keeping track of essential and core elements like membership, billing, utilization records, care delivery, and plan performance.

Given those challenges, we knew that a pure and direct per capita prepayment model for the doctors and hospitals was our only hope. We had to achieve absolute simplicity of cash flow to make the program work. Transplanting a typical fee-for-service-based American insurance model to Uganda was absolutely destined to fail. The doctors in Uganda needed to be prepaid, not post-paid. That decision about prepayment approaches was the difference between success and guaranteed failure. So what, exactly, does that decision mean?

Typical American health insurers — and almost all United States government Medicare and Medicaid programs — generally use an administratively complex, post-care, incident-specific, procedure-focused, claims-based approach to paying for care. A claims-based fee-for-service approach creates floods of paperwork to, from, and between at least three parties — the caregivers, the members, and the plan. The whole American fee-for-service insurance process is awash in paper, with multiple pieces and layers of new paper generated by each individual incident of care.

The complex and extensive steps involved in a typical American claims-based, paper-dependent billing and payment approach are known to us all. A patient goes to a provider for care. The provider checks eligibility with the plan — usually by phone and sometimes by computer. The provider delivers care to the patient and then fills out a claim form. That claim form is then mailed to the plan. Someone in the plan manually keys the claim into a computer and the claim is then "examined" to see who owes who money. If the claim is eligible for full or partial payment, a check is produced. That check is mailed to the care provider, along with a description of the benefits and an explanation of payment. A copy of the claims document and a copy of the check is usually also sent to the member. For each claim.

If a co-payment or deductible is involved, the plan also notifies the patient and provider of the co-payment amount, sending yet another piece of paper through the mail. The provider then also tends to send the patient a bill for any co-payment or deductible amount that turns out to be due from the patient.

That's for a clean claim. A simple claim. Not all claims are clean or simple. Claims with missing information or coding errors take more steps, more paper, more time, and more administrative expense. Claims with ambiguous eligibility or care network sites can create layers of inquiry and require additional paperwork.

The entire process is recorded for posterity, the regulators, the bookkeepers, and the courts in multiple physical settings — in the plan files, the providers' files, and the members' files. All of that paper takes up a lot of space and costs a lot of money.

That's just the paper associated with claims. It takes more pieces of paper to get each member enrolled into the plan. It takes even more paper to get premiums billed and paid. Typical insurers bill the members regularly, collect the money, reconcile the bills against the receipts, and update the various membership files constantly. Those processes also each tend to generate a lot of paper. And cost a lot of money. ID cards tend to be sent by the insurer to each member, usually with a separate ID card for each member of each family. The whole ID card process adds some real expense as well.

Simply transplanting all of that typical American insurance

fee-for-service-based paper flow to Uganda would have been an expensive, dysfunctional, and economically unworkable mistake.

The Ugandan Model Is Almost Paper Free

So the actual plan and administrative approach that we decided to use in Uganda was much simpler. It's almost paperless. We eliminated "claims." The providers are prepaid a lump sum of money each month for each patient, rather than paid a fee after each incident of care. There's only one very small computer in the process for each local combination of provider and plan. The programming for that computer was developed jointly by HealthPartners and Oracle Systems. Oracle Corporation, by the way, made a much-appreciated commitment to working with HealthPartners to develop a small stand-alone system for a computer that can simultaneously run the key functions of a micro health plan and maintain on-site provider records for the caregivers. Very little paper is involved at any step in the process.

How does that Ugandan approach avoid a typical American flow of paper? Each local plan places the computer system itself at the provider site and turns operations of the computer over to the contracted care provider. That eliminates the need for a plan processor or staff. It almost wipes out that entire administrative cost for the plan. As care is delivered, information about the care is put directly into the on-site computer by the care provider. There are no bills or claims involved. No paperwork. No letters or stamps. The monthly reports about the actual use of care by co-op members that result are entirely electronic. No one double punches or triple punches any bills or claims data.

The system stands alone and is used jointly by all parties. The whole process is electronic — not paper. The local plan, by contract, has access at any time to the computer and its contents. Reports are generated regularly for the co-op by each provider.

Oracle Corporation contributed significant time, talent, and resources to help HealthPartners develop the system. The actual startup and development costs to design and build the micro system were relatively large by Ugandan standards — nearly $500,000 from all parties. But the system can now be set up on each provider site for the cost of a processor and a keyboard. One processor per care system is more than enough. Since the care system runs the computer system, there are no related expenses for the co-op health plan itself. That helped.

Prepayment — Not Claims — Is the Key

The real secret to success in reducing administrative costs is to prepay — or "capitate" — providers. That streamlined, administratively elegant operational model is possible only because the actual payment arrangements for physicians and hospitals are very deliberately not built around paying for each individual unit of care one piece at a time. It is not a claims-based model. It is a prepaid model. It buys packages of care — not pieces of care. The whole Ugandan health cooperative approach is built around negotiated monthly prepayment levels for each local micro health plan member.

Each local co-op, of course, needs certain levels of additional administrative services to run the program — like current co-op membership lists. Where does that membership data come from? From each co-op. Each local co-op provides the membership data necessary to feed each local computer system. Again, it's a one-step process — with information going directly from the local, elected co-op leader to the local computer system. The co-op leaders work with one monthly printout from the local computer system to track current membership and to update, correct, and add data. It's one summary piece of paper about the current membership status for every member of the co-op — not separate bills and paper for each.

Co-payments used by each plan are negotiated annually

HITTING OUR 10-CENT TARGET •

and then printed on the member ID card so that the whole billing/adjudication/communication process for co-pays is bypassed. Co-payments are fixed in price — not a percentage of a fee, so no fees or payments need to be calculated at the time of care. It's the simplest possible payment process. Very elegant and very functional.

The ID cards are issued one per family, not one per person. The ID card is actually a laminated, 4x6 photo of the family — with the family picture on one side and all relevant member data on the back. The names of each family member are listed on the card, along with the co-op name and the relevant benefits.

In a country where families of 10 or more people are fairly common — particularly if there is more than one wife — we knew that we couldn't possibly afford a process that generated separate ID cards for each family member. The ID card issuance alone would wipe out the full 10 percent administrative cost budget if we used the same approach we used in America. We could only afford one ID card per family — hand-delivered rather than mailed. We couldn't afford postage, and the postal system in rural Uganda wasn't particularly useful in any case.

We also knew that any version of ID cards with no photos wouldn't do us a lot of good in preventing fraudulent use by the patients. Since the caregivers obviously do not know every resident of the local greater community by sight or name, and since most Ugandans have little or no paper identification or documentation, there was some initial concern that a plan member might take pity on a non-member neighbor with a sick child and simply let that child fraudulently use their ID card.

That is a very practical concern. That particular behavior is not unheard of in the United States. Done skillfully, the culprits are often not detected — much less deterred — particularly in larger United States cities and open-panel insurance plans. It's somewhat rare, but it happens.

69

Presenting a card to a new health plan member
during the ID card ceremony.

We thought those risks would be much higher in Uganda, because almost no one has any insurance, and the temptation might be great to bring the proverbial "aunt from Masaka" to the clinic and pass her off as a family member to get care.

So what did we do? We issued family photo ID cards, one per family. The photos are taken with disposable cameras at gatherings sponsored by the co-ops. I personally have participated in several photo sessions, taking the photos and sharing in the festivities.

The photos are each then laminated onto a family enrollment ID form. The picture is on the front of the laminated card. The names of all the family members and the coverage dates are on the back. The computer-printed ID form lists all the family members and contains key information about the co-op benefits and plan status. The lamination prevents the members from modifying the document in any way.

The family photo ID cards serve four main purposes:

1) They eliminate a lot of individual cards.

2) They are very durable, so they hold up much better than paper in a wet and wallet-free society.

3) They give the local caregiver a visual way of identifying each child.

4) Because each co-op tends to self-police the process to make sure no "ringers" are covered, the photos help keep care use limited to the people who are legitimate plan members.

In a paperless culture, the ID cards are the only family photographs that most of the members have ever had. Expired ID cards are retained in many families as family mementos. We hope that the lamination glue doesn't cause the pictures to deteriorate over time.

We initially intended to have the whole photo process handled with a digital camera and a print-out of the ID card. Getting the photo printers to function properly and cheaply in rural Uganda has been a problem, so we've returned to a standard film format for the photos. Digital photos also still take up quite a lot of computer capacity. We were planning to revisit that issue whenever a technology change made the purely digital process more workable.

ID cards are a basic health plan function. Every health plan in every setting in the world needs some form of ID card so that providers of care know whether or not a patient actually has coverage. The approach we decided to use in Uganda was as minimalist as we could go — and it actually has worked quite well. Only an all-electronic system would be simpler — and that isn't yet possible in an environment without computers or consistent electricity.

From an administrative perspective, one major goal of the Ugandan plan design is to have each piece of relevant data touched only once on its way into the system. Once the data is in the system, all parties — co-op, administration, and care providers — have equal access to all of the reports and outputs of that data.

We took other shortcuts as well.

Premium charges in Uganda are often by quarter, not by month, for example. Monthly bills are a bit more difficult to administer cheaply. We also avoided postage with a passion. Postage alone, if we mailed the monthly bills, would devour the entire premium. So we also eliminated postage. How? The bills are hand delivered by the co-op leaders.

In Uganda, we have time, but no cash. So we set up the cash collection to be done by each co-op, in person by the co-op leaders, as part of its normal business. For the dairy co-ops, we received a weekly allocation of milk from each member.

Or, to be more specific, when the co-op received milk from the farmers, part originally went to the co-op dues, part went to co-op expenses (like veterinarians and cow medicine), and the rest was given to the farmers as take-home pay. Once we got the co-op started, a specific part also went to the health co-op fund. Once a month, that fund gives the accumulated premium to the local contracted caregiver, along with a checklist of which farmers were paid up in the plan.

A similar process takes place with the tea and coffee co-ops — except that the premium in those co-ops is generally paid for months in advance at harvest time.

The computer system we installed keeps track of which families are paid up for how long.

If anyone is behind in payments, that list is given to the local co-op leader, usually the person carrying the title of "chair." The local chair then takes on the task of following up to see if the members are leaving the plan or if they just, possibly, had a dry month for milk or a bad harvest for their tea.

In either case, the expense for that follow-up visit doesn't fall on the plan. It's part of the co-op leader's job.

That approach eliminates both monthly billing and follow-up on late payments.

Is it actually possible to administer a micro health plan for a dime? It is, at the local level only. It is possible only if the co-op members and care providers both do a lot of work.

There are really two levels of administrative dollars involved in the Uganda co-ops — the ongoing local costs of running each co-op, and the central development and support effort costs. Those are two different budgets. It is highly unlikely that the initial central development costs needed to set up new co-ops and new provider networks will ever be adequately funded from the dime per month. There is a high probability, however, that the local, ongoing operational costs in each site can be perpetually funded by the current equivalent of that dime. The trick is to duplicate nothing, mail nothing, and produce as little paper as possible. The entire system has to be elegantly de-signed and simple to a fault. Since the provider has to keep a record of care in any case, the answer to multiple layers of data input costs is to simply use that sole provider site record as the single source of all data. This is, of course, possible only when the provider is a full partner working as a member of the team to make the co-op a success.

At some future point — when e-commerce has been broadly introduced to Uganda — it will be possible for remote consult-ants, coordinators, and analysts to tie into those little stand-alone systems to glean data and check performance. For now, that level of offsite data review has to be done periodically, and external review can only be done by disc.

It needs to be noted that there have been some pressures in Uganda to move to a claims-based, more typically American fee-for-service insurance model. That suggestion has been made most often by providers of care who would like to be paid full fees and by people who would like to make more than one care system available to each co-op member. The incredible addi-tional cost burden of that administrative data expansion and additional paper flow makes it impossible and unaffordable to offer that level of provider choice at this point. But, there's no reason to believe that a broader network with more choices can't be set up in the relatively near future in a couple of sites, if the co-ops can negotiate a deal that lets each provider receive prepayment for the specific members who select them.

The challenge will be to have the electronic membership systems between care sites "talk" to each other so it is clear where each co-op member is authorized to receive care. In the current, pure, single-care-site selection model, that computer-to-computer conversation and coordination isn't needed because the entire family for each member is at one care site with all data for each co-op on one care-site computer.

The Co-Op Leaders Play a Key Role

There are shortcuts to administrating a health plan but, in the end, each key piece of work still needs to be done.

The basic administrative model for each local health plan in Uganda has to accomplish just about all of the administrative tasks done by American health plans. The administrative process in both countries has to identify who is covered and for what. It needs to list benefits, send out premium billings, pay providers, and track the utilization of care. The system in both countries needs to maintain eligibility records as well as care delivery records. In Uganda, all of those goals need to be accomplished with no post office, no stamps, no phone system, and a minimum of paper.

So, as I noted earlier, a lot of heavy lifting is done by the co-op members and their leaders. The co-op leaders enroll members and collect the premiums. The co-op leaders also use the single local provider-run computer to keep track of co-op care expenses. As the process is set up, there is just a single computer system in each care site that handles all record keeping for the co-op as well as for the care site. Certain reports come out of that system regularly to keep the co-op leaders informed about utilization levels, membership status, and expense levels.

Other records are used to track utilization, and to help the caregivers deliver better and more consistent care.

Central staff from the Kampala office of Uganda Health Cooperatives helps each site implement the system. That central staff then works with both the co-op leaders and the local caregivers to help keep the process on track. To date, local hospitals and care systems have been extremely grateful for the computers and the Oracle system. Up to now, medical records in much of Uganda have either been nonexistent or consisted of simple sheets of paper with very few pieces of information written on them.

The new system gives caregivers a lot more data about their practices and their care.

Separate chapters discuss the roles and duties of the co-op leaders, the Ugandan Health Co-op staff, the local caregivers, and the American consultants who have been helping with this process.

Overall, the administrative goal is clear. It is to provide all administration well, and do it for just a few pennies. At this point, it appears as though there is a good chance of achieving that goal for a very long time, as long as the co-op system can continue to be based on prepayment and a local team effort between the caregivers and the co-ops. Avoiding fee-for-service is essential.

Instead of having individual claims forms filled out and sent to us by our care providers, we simply require the physicians by contract to code into our local computer system a brief report on each member encounter. We want that particular computer data set about the care both for quality of care purposes and for cost estimates. The caregivers want it so they can keep track of the amount of work they are doing. Those reports also typically show up as evidence about the volumes of needed care when capitation negotiations are held with the provider for the next year. Again, to avoid paperwork and plan expense, we put the computer in the hospital or clinic and have the input done by the care provider. Plan personnel only look at the output.

So that's how you run a health plan for a dime a month. You simplify. Simplify. Simplify.

The overall benefit design is simple. One benefit package per community. To keep administrative costs low, we use almost no paper. Cash flow and billing is paperless and delegated to the co-ops. Utilization reporting is paperless and delegated to the caregivers. Our systems allow them both to do their job cheaply and easily. Claims are eliminated with prepayment. ID cards are replaced by photos — generally taken with disposable, one-use cameras. Contracting doesn't involve any lawyers.

Our central staff helps set things up and then helps keep things running.

And the local administrative cost is actually coming in at 10 percent of premium.

There are learnings there for the United States.

Chapter Six
Paying the Providers

*Prepaid caregivers increase their emphasis on disease
prevention rather than just disease treatment.*

The HealthPartners team decided very early in the planning
process that the only possible payment approach for care providers that had any chance of success was "prepayment." As noted in
Chapter Five, that was the only approach that gave us a chance of
reducing the administrative burden for the Ugandan health co-ops
to manageable levels. It also was the best way, we believed, to
align the financial incentives of the care providers with the health
and care incentives of the co-op members. It was a key discussion, so it might be useful to look, in a little more detail, at why
that particular mechanism was selected.

For starters, we knew from our experience in the United
States that fully cooperating, carefully selected, participating
providers of care were needed to make each local plan a success
and we also knew that these providers would need to be paid.

That's pretty basic thinking. Health Plan 101. The delivery of
care requires caregivers. The questions were — How should the
caregivers be involved? Who should they be? What role or roles
should they play? In order to create care delivery mechanisms for
our micro co-ops in Uganda, we needed to figure out how best to

select, recruit, and then appropriately involve local caregivers in the plan operation. We ended up with prepayment as our preferred financial arrangement, but we didn't just look at prepayments as the only option. We considered other alternatives as well. Deciding on the best approach for Uganda caregiver selection and payment involved looking both at several United States models of caregiver involvement and — of primary importance — at the reality of health care delivery and provider availability in Uganda.

The approach we selected is not the usual approach in the United States. Health insurance in the United States has evolved over the past two decades into several different species of programs, plans, and provider payment mechanisms. Some health insurers in the United States actually own clinics and hire various care providers. That's a relatively rare model in our country. It's a very good model — but it's far from the norm. At the other extreme, some health insurers have absolutely no relationship with caregivers, other than to receive claims forms and pay claims. That complete separation model is also now a relatively uncommon approach. Most plan/provider relationships in the United States fall between those extremes. Most payers in this country now choose to contract in some way with caregivers and most now create some form of caregiver networks for their customers to use. Those contracted networks generally have negotiated price discounts relative to provider fees as their key financial cash flow component. In our own co-op plan in Minnesota, we had a mixed model. We owned clinics and directly employed more than 600 physicians. So we were both a health insurer and a provider of care. We also contracted with nearly 10,000 more local physicians. Most of the contracted physicians in Minnesota were part of "prepaid" contracts rather than pure fee-for-service arrangements. So, we knew from direct experience how both the contracted and direct employment models work. (At

Kaiser Permanente, we have eight regional health plans that contract exclusively with eight very large regional medical groups. The entire Kaiser Permanente entity, in total, owns 32 hospitals and employs more than 140,000 people — including more than 15,000 physicians who own and lead the eight Permanente Medical Groups.) So, in both my old job and my present one, I have worked closely with and believe strongly in the models of care and financing that are much more tightly integrated between the health plan and the caregiver. But, we did not simply assume that was the only model that could work in Uganda.

As HealthPartners staff looking at African health care, we knew that our Ugandan model wouldn't initially generate enough cash for the local co-ops to actually build their own clinics, hire their own caregivers, or own their own hospitals. We also knew that we wouldn't have enough patient volume to create exclusive 'Kaiser Permanente-like' relationships with local physicians. We didn't have enough initial cash flow to actually recruit and hire physicians to take care of the co-op members. We concluded, therefore, that we needed to do deals with local caregivers — deals that encouraged the local caregivers to provide the best care in the most efficient way — with a focus on disease prevention wherever possible. Since directly hiring physicians was not going to be possible, we knew that the only way we would get good deals for our members would be to enter into some kind of positive, mutually beneficial, clearly spelled-out financial relation-ships and formal contracts with local doctors and hospitals that paid them enough money to create a win/win situation for the co-ops and the providers of care. The question was: what kinds of contracts? And what kind of deal?

Again, we had some United States models to think about. We didn't want to bring an unworkable fee-based approach to Uganda just because it was popular in the United States. As noted earlier, in most cases in the United States, where provider networks exist, the contracted caregivers simply charge discounted fees to the plans they deal with. In that case, the plans are the primary "insurers" and they pay "claims" to the care providers for all care that is delivered. In a number of other American situations where there are contracts between the health plans and the providers of care, the caregivers themselves are "prepaid" or "capitated" — receiving a fixed amount of money each month for every patient that selects them as caregivers. The prepaid providers agree to provide all needed care in exchange for that prepayment, or "capitation." In that capitated model, the caregivers share in the risk for the cost and efficiency levels of care because the payment mechanism is a fixed, pre-negotiated monthly fee (or capitation) paid per member — rather than a separate fee paid for each individual care encounter by each member.

Those options — and several other blends of those two approaches — needed to be considered as we tried to figure out a model that would work in Kasizi, Bushenga, and greater Kampala.

In putting together our initial plan, we felt four main structural questions had to be resolved. Choices had to be made in several key areas.

"Pre-" or "Post-" Paid Doctors?

The first choice dealt with the issue of "prepayment" versus "post-payment" of providers. As noted earlier, this was a fundamental difference in approach. It has huge ramifications for how any health plan is managed and administered. Both prepaid and post-paid models are used in the United States. In a post-payment approach, providers provide care to a patient and then — after the fact — send a bill to the insurer for each incident of care. The insurer then carefully examines each bill to see if the service is covered by the patient's insurance benefit package. If it is covered, the insurer writes a check to the caregiver for whatever fee level the provider is entitled to receive. Usually, those fee levels have been negotiated in advance between the health plan and the caregiver.

That "fee-for-service" model is how most health care is insured in the United States. It has the advantage of paying providers exactly for whatever care is received by each patient.

Post-Payment

Post-payment — or fee-for-service medicine — has two major and obvious disadvantages if you want to incent better care or save administrative dollars. Those disadvantages can, in fact, be crippling if you want to reduce administrative costs to a dime a month. A primary disadvantage of that fee-for-service payment model is that it financially incents the caregivers to deliver excess and unnecessary units of care in order to make more money. Multiple American studies have verified beyond any doubt that the problem of inappropriate, sometimes wasteful, fee-incentivized care exists. Fee-for-service providers are not paid for "curing" the patient or for preventing disease or for reducing the complications of a disease. They are simply paid for procedures done for each patient. Outcomes are irrelevant in the payment process. Providers of care in that fee-for-service model make money by doing volumes of procedures — not by improving health. We wanted a model in Uganda that required the providers to deliver all necessary care, but did not create perverse and unaffordable financial incentives to do unnecessary care. We also wanted a model where the provider made money by keeping people healthy, rather than making a profit only when the patients are sick. Those are very different types of incentives.

The second problem — an even bigger one in Uganda when we were trying to design a health plan that could be administered for 10 cents a month — is that post-payment care models with fee-for-service payments always involve a ton of administration. The administration costs are huge. They involve a lot of paperwork — a huge amount of paperwork. Think again about what I noted in the last chapter about all of the paperwork that needs to be done. In a fee-for-service system, each new incident of care generates a new claim. Each claim generates separate paperwork. Claims have to be mailed from provider to insurer. Each claim has to be examined by someone to see if the benefit is covered. Each approved claim results in a check. Someone has to write all of those checks. They need to be mailed. Each rejected claim results in at least two rejection letters — one to the patient and one to the caregiver. The paperwork and administrative processes inherently involved in post-paid fee-for-service care are staggering — going well beyond anything a dime could handle. That's how most American health care insurance is handled, and that's the primary reason why American health care administrative costs are the highest in the world.

In this country — in prepaid plans like HealthPartners and Kaiser Permanente — a huge portion of that paperwork has been eliminated. HealthPartners now pre-pays for most care and then receives more than 90 percent of all claims electronically. We set up that electronic claims input process so we wouldn't have to handle all of that expensive paper every time care is delivered. That paperless system saves both care providers and the plan a lot of administrative money. At Kaiser Permanente, we have always had a very low cost, paperless system. At this point, we are also installing a computerized automated medical record system that will directly feed the insurance system work flow with no paper and no hands touching the information — again, cutting administrative costs significantly. Those processes are all electronically supported. The electronic infrastructure needed to achieve either of those approaches obviously didn't exist in Uganda in any site we had visited, however. So, we created one based on prepayment.

The decision was not actually very difficult. A traditional

insurance claims-based, fee-for-service system would obviously have had huge cost disadvantages for Ugandans — particularly if we wanted to administer the plan for a dime a month.

The third problem of fee-for-service-based care compared to a "prepaid" capitated system was, if anything, even more important: incentives to improve health and prevent disease. A prepaid provider has a very direct, clearly understood incentive to improve patient health — to help prevent malaria, avoid dysentery, and avoid parasitic infection. A physician who is prepaid has a financial incentive to help all patients get mosquito nets for people's beds to help them avoid malaria, for example. A fee-for-service, post-paid physician has no way of being directly or indirectly paid for those kinds of pro-active programs and services and that level of preventive health thinking. We desperately needed that level of pro-active, disease-prevention thinking in Uganda, so a capitated model that created physician incentives for improving population health obviously made the most sense.

Those facts of economic life brought us quickly to "prepayment" as a way of paying the doctors and hospitals.

Prepayment

Prepayment, done well, is not a complicated approach. It can be elegantly simple, in fact.

How does it work?

In a prepayment model, the provider is paid a flat sum of money each month in advance for each member of the plan. In exchange for the monthly prepayment amount, the provider in a pure prepayment model simply provides all of the care outlined in the member's contract. No claims are filed. No paper is generated. Only one check is written — one per month — and that single check covers many people — all co-op members who have enrolled and selected that particular caregiver.

That process eliminates a lot of forms, processes, and huge

volumes of claims checks. It eliminates individual claims as well as the need to do individual claims adjudication. The providers still need to keep a record of all care delivered, but that record can be electronically kept by the provider and simply examined periodically and retrospectively by the plan as a report, rather than processed piece-by-piece as a stack of claims.

If we wanted to keep administrative costs to a dime, prepayment was obviously the only way to go. The challenge, of course, was to persuade Ugandan providers of care who had always been paid on an after-the-fact fee-for-service basis that a lump sum monthly prepayment for each patient was also a very good way to get paid. The challenge was also to help prepaid caregivers increase their emphasis on disease prevention rather than just disease treatment. As you will see, that process was well received by Ugandan physicians.

The good news about working through the negotiated payment levels was that we knew from talking to various rural Ugandan caregivers that 25 to 40 percent of their current patients actually don't pay their bills at all under the old non-insurance, patient direct pay fee-for-service model. High numbers of patients were non-payers — bad debt in American terms. Many paid only part of the bill. So, our negotiating strategy with physicians and hospitals was to persuade the Ugandan caregivers to accept "prepayment" from the co-ops by telling them, "Getting dependable monthly prepayment from 100 percent of your co-op patients is far better than getting partial and sporadic post-payment from roughly half of the people you already care for."

As we had hoped, that argument turned out to be very effective with every caregiver with whom we met. That's not surprising. It was just common sense. These are very smart people. And, very practical people. The rural Ugandan doctors each knew from years of experience how difficult it was to collect money from most of their patients. This new approach eliminated bad debt for all patients who joined the co-op. It created a dependable monthly cash flow. For the patients, it completely eliminated the whole onerous fee-for-service billing process. It also — as a side benefit — eliminated those awkward and often unpleasant situations where a debtor patient — seeing the doctor come into the village market or local church — felt a need to duck out the back way, to avoid an embarrassing moment. That sort of financially strained doctor/patient relationship doesn't generally lead to particularly effective follow-up care.

Most usefully, for the caregivers, prepayment gave them a steady, dependable stream of cash. Once they began caring for members of the local co-op health plan, the caregivers knew that they would receive the prepayment amount on a fixed date every month. For many Ugandan health care providers, that capitation was the only regular local source of cash they had ever had.

As we had hoped, that new approach actually did help local providers economically. That new and dependable cash flow let some caregivers expand their facilities and practices — depending on the steady prepayment cash flow from the co-op to service the resulting debt.

So how did the local Ugandan physicians and hospitals respond? They liked the new co-op health plans. They strongly encouraged local people to join the co-op plans once they were set up. Provider support was real and effective. Again, there are interesting and informative parallels in the United States. Strong provider support was actually the main reason that the original Blue Cross and Blue Shield plans were set up in the United States. They were created by doctors and hospitals to create a prepayment revenue source to help those doctors and hospitals stay solvent and avoid patient debt in the Great Depression. The original Blue Plans would never have succeeded without that direct provider support.

"Service Benefits" or "Procedure Fees"?

The second major financial issue to resolve was whether to assign a fixed fee value to each provider service or to use a "service benefit" approach to figure out what was covered. What does that mean? In a "service benefit" model, the plan and provider agree to cover a defined list of services for a population of patients in exchange for a fixed, pre-negotiated aggregate amount of money rather than assigning a cash value to each service and then charging separately for each service.

In a service benefit model, the agreement is to provide all of the services that a member might need from the pre-negotiated set of defined services. One of the best features of a "service benefit" approach is that the provider doesn't need to go through the administrative work of assigning a price to each individual procedure or incident of care. It's a simple model to administer.

So, in Uganda, we decided to just use a pure service benefit approach — stating for example, that "maternity care is a prepaid covered service," rather than "we will pay or credit 15,000 Ugandan shillings to each provider for each normal delivery."

Again, the record keeping is much simpler and cleaner without the pre-negotiated fee assignments and without any risk share follow-up. That's how we started the plan. It's a smart and good model. Unfortunately, we later found ourselves forced into the fee-based scorecard business to some degree. Malaria epidemics, for example, caused some caregivers to deliver twice as much care in some years as paid for by the "capitation." As we will discuss later, we ended up with some risk-sharing features that required the providers to do more record keeping. Other parties — foreign governments — who liked the program offered a form of catastrophic cost reinsurance to our plans. More on that topic later. But initially, to keep matters simple, we wanted to use pure service benefits in both our member contracts and provider contracts. Where that can be done, it's a better, cleaner, easier approach to administer.

One major advantage that generally results from combining prepayment with general service agreements is that that approach to prepayment encourages much higher levels of provider flexibility and creativity relative to care. Whenever fee schedules exist in the world, they always tend to make care delivery more rigid. Why? Because care is very much limited to the fee schedule list of acceptable services. Those fee lists also inherently dictate care priorities — sometimes in pervasive ways. Preventive care generally isn't well rewarded by American fee schedules; so, in our country, extensive and systematic prevention tends not to be done. Innovative approaches to preventive care are less likely to happen.

HealthPartners had benefited greatly by being a prepaid plan in the United States. That payment system allows for a much more flexible, patient-focused use of resources. So, when HealthPartners had a patient with congestive heart failure (CHF) for example, care for that patient wasn't limited to the strictly defined set of services found on a Medicare fee schedule. Medicare has always used a fairly rigid outline of acceptable medical procedures for its fee-for-service payment program. But, HealthPartners was prepaid by Medicare on a monthly basis for each patient to provide the care that each patient needed. So, HealthPartners used that flexibility and long ago created a whole new approach to team-based care for patients with CHF that involved dedicated nurses, group meetings, telephone consults, and even special electronic scales that we put in the homes of some patients with CHF. The scales actually call HealthPartners to warn the doctors and nurses if the patient has an alarming weight gain that could indicate a CHF crisis might be starting.

As a result of that total program, HealthPartners' caregiver teams cut those terrifying, painful, life-threatening, and extremely expensive CHF crises by more than 80 percent for our members. That's an incredible improvement in the quality of life for those patients. If we had been simply stuck with the list of services authorized by a pure traditional Medicare insurance post-payment fee-for-service model, and if the care had to be delivered only under the more rigid Medicare fee-based procedure list and rules, that wonderful, patient-focused, life-saving program would not exist. It did not exist for Medicare's non-HMO patients when we invented that approach for CHF care. The Medicare fee list did not pay for group meetings, nurse-level care coordination, phone follow-ups, or electronic, telephone-linked scales. Five times as many patients with CHF in the Minnesota plan would go through the hellish experience of drowning in their own fluids if HealthPartners wasn't committed to the flexibility given to plan physicians by prepayment and service benefits. Far too many non-HMO Medicare patients, even today in most of the country, are five times more likely to go through that horrible experience. That whole CHF program was widely publicized, and now has many clones in other parts of the country. Medicare now endorses most of the needed services. But, the new treatment approach only evolved because care systems like HealthPartners and Kaiser Permanente were prepaid and therefore able to innovate in care delivery beyond the limitations of a fee list.

So, knowing first hand how that whole prepaid, service benefit process works, we also strongly favored prepayment in Uganda. We didn't want a rigid fee schedule that limited local provider flexibility. We wanted the Ugandan doctors to have both an incentive to prevent disease, and the ability to be flexible in determining the most efficient ways of delivering care. As you will see, it worked just as we had hoped. Ugandan caregivers became very prevention-focused and creative in their use of resources. (Likewise, at Kaiser Permanente, we may well have won more awards than anyone in America for the effectiveness of our disease management programs and preventive care. The flexibility given to the caregiver by the prepayment method is a key to our success.)

Prepayment works.

The model we chose for Uganda was an approach that involved very close partnerships with local caregivers — physicians and hospitals — who were prepaid to avoid the hassle and administrative waste involved in claims processing, and who were incented to provide both best care and preventive care to their patients.

Ugandan caregivers loved that model for reasons discussed in the next chapter.

Chapter Seven
Provider/Plan Cooperation=Success

*An anemic child is less likely to be able
to withstand a case of malaria.*

It's impossible to overstate the importance of having close, effective, and mutually beneficial partnership relationships with physicians to make this model of care a success. No aspect of creating health care co-ops is more important than the relationship with the care delivery system used by the co-ops for its members.

The most sophisticated, well-designed micro health structure will fail if it can't create a workable, win-win relationship with an appropriate local provider of care. Care is the key factor that people want. The whole point of creating local health care cooperatives is to give people access to better, more affordable care. That can't be done without health care providers who participate in enlightened and mutually beneficial ways with the program.

In the Uganda Health Cooperative model, caregivers play five indispensable roles:

1) They provide care.
2) They accept prepayment in exchange for that care.
3) They maintain the key front-level administrative system.
4) They agree to work on preventing disease and systematically improving the health of the local co-op members.

5) They participate as leaders in the development of quality of care and care improvement programs.

Providing care is first on the list because receiving care is the first priority of the patients. The whole process is about helping the people who need care actually get that care. Only caregivers can provide that care. What kind of care is needed? To be part of these micro health schemes, we believe a caregiver should be able and willing to provide both hospital and medical care in the actual geographic area served by each micro health group.

It is, of course, possible to set up a prepayment fund that provides only medical care — or even only hospital care — but that approach is much less desirable for obvious reasons. It's not what the patients really want. People want a full range of locally available care — hospital and medical. Simply setting up a limited provider configuration — maybe under a partial prepayment approach — would not meet the health care needs of too many patients. Also, a partial set of services is much less likely to create the kind of coordinated interaction between hospital and medical care that results in the best outcomes for patients. Ideally, the participating care partner for each local co-op should be either a hospital that employs physicians or a local physician or medical group who owns a hospital. That "vertical integration" of hospital and medical care creates a single, highly integrated provider business unit for the co-op to work with.

It is, we found, possible for a new local health care co-op in a village to actually serve as a local matchmaker — helping to create new, synergistic partnerships between local independent physicians and a hospital. Done well and structured appropriately, those caregiver partnerships can create the functional equivalent of a fully integrated doctor/hospital system. The financial issues involved in prepayment approaches can become much more complicated if the local doctors and hospitals don't have a direct business linkage — and they can be very complicated if the

Meeting with an agricultural co-op to discuss their joining the health care co-op at the chair of the agriculture cooperative's home.

provider entities who work with the co-op directly compete with each other in some way for the patients or for actual plan revenue.

For optimal set-up effectiveness and long-term stability, we concluded that the preferred local provider partner entity should be a combined doctor/hospital organization — with at least one full-time doctor and a constantly staffed hospital. Ideally, the partner organization will have several doctors, with at least one physician regularly performing general surgery.

The standards for determining whether or not a local health care co-op should work with a given local hospital are based on common sense and good judgment. Is the provider sufficiently local? Are the needed services available from the provider? Is the caregiver trusted? Is the care site well run? A key issue is support. Mutual support. Will the two organizations proactively support one another? Some local standards need to be fairly flexible. There is a wide variation in what is available in care delivery services in various communities in developing countries. In Uganda, in some settings, the best hospital care for many people from many kilometers around may have only partial access to electricity, no running water, and limited food available for hospitalized patients. Those kinds of issues, we concluded, should not cause the new health plan to reject entering into a relationship with the hospital — particularly if there are no other local hospital options. Those hospitals often still manage to provide surprisingly high levels of critically necessary care for some conditions, and they have saved a great many lives. They may not meet American care standards in many ways, but for the person whose life they save, they definitely make an important difference. Simply applying a western world, industrialized country's checklist to evaluating local hospitals would be a mistake in many, if not all, cases. As we were putting the program together, we decided we needed to play the game with the cards dealt — not refuse to play because we wish we had better cards.

So, how do we choose a specific local hospital or a physician as a care partner in Uganda? We usually asked the local co-op organizers to do that for themselves. They know who they want. The local co-op members generally already know the character and service levels of each local caregiver. Local knowledge is very important.

So, our basic standard was that if the local co-op leaders designated a particular hospital or physician group as their preferred choice for receiving care, we believed that those local leaders are clearly the best people to make that particular decision and we then negotiated on their behalf with the hospital or medical group they chose. We don't ask for that decision on day one, however. We first spend considerable time with the local co-op members, helping them understand exactly what role the hospital/physician entity will play in the new co-op delivery approach. Those context-setting conversations definitely help guide the co-ops in their decision-making process.

Personal reputation, credibility, and competence are areas best judged by people who live in the area and know the local caregivers well. Those intangible but critically important factors are generally hard or even impossible to determine in a "site visit" situation by outside people, particularly outside people whose only relevant context is American health care.

Prepayment

As noted earlier, prepayment is a critically important part of the whole micro health approach we used in Uganda. If the local care providers in any setting insist on being paid a fee for each procedure, the prepayment model we use will not work. Not to belabor the point, but that fee-for-service approach would be administratively crippling, perversely incented, and financially unstable. A fee-based approach would require each mini health co-op to collect a premium, put it into a bank account, and then pay individual provider fees from that account as care is delivered. As noted earlier in this book, that approach is operationally messy and very risky as well as administratively burdensome. If the total cost of local care delivered and paid for under that fee-based model ever exceeds the pot of available money, the co-op would immediately go broke. There are no financial reserves. Who would pick up the debt for an insolvent, fee-for-service co-op? Who would pay for the care that people received on the assumption that an insurer would be standing behind them financially? And, as noted earlier, it's important to remember that any time a separate fee-for-service claim has to be filed, administrative money is wasted processing that claim. Those processing costs can add up — often ranging from $5-$20 per claim in the United States just to process the necessary paperwork.

In the United States, the overall cash flow for health care is so rich that spending $5-$20 of administrative costs to process each and every claim is much less noticeable. It's only a few percent of the total premium paid. In Uganda, $10 represents roughly 18,000 shillings. Keep in mind that one month's total family premium is 4,000 shillings, and the cost problem of individual claims administration becomes pretty obvious.

So, to make the program actually work, the care provider must be willing to agree to accept a prepayment amount as full compensation for delivering care to the co-op members.

Why would a provider in Uganda accept prepayment? Why would an under-funded, cash-poor, rural Ugandan hospital agree to become, in effect, an insurer? Because prepayment can be a very good deal financially for the hospital or doctor. For starters, as mentioned above, prepayment is guaranteed money. It is a steady income. Dependable income. It's there for the hospital every month. Since 99 percent of Ugandans have no health insurance, and since per capita income is running at $270 a year, quite a few patients can't afford to pay their medical bills — even when the bills are relatively very low.

In fact, as noted earlier, we quickly learned that anywhere from 30 to 60 percent of the total patient billing for a typical rural Uganda hospital usually ends up as bad debt/unpaid bills.

So, a new prepayment approach that gives providers any regular cash flow that actually consistently exceeds 50 percent of their total expected billing revenue from a specific set of people is actually a good deal financially. "Prepayment" that consistently and dependably covers 75 percent of a hospital bill is quite a bit better for the local hospital than a direct-pay, bad-debt scenario where uninsured patients only pay 50 percent of the bill. Guaranteed prepayment is also quite a bit more dependable than having local, cash-poor patients owe money that they can't possibly pay until harvest time, if ever.

The co-op money is not only guaranteed, it is also timely. It actually comes ahead of the care — allowing hospitals to pay their nurses and allowing doctors to stock up on needed drugs.

So, local caregivers tend to like any program that generates a dependable supply of local money.

Local Money and Local Services

Local money is actually another key concept. It is rare in most rural Ugandan settings. A high percentage of rural Ugandan hospitals depend on charity from abroad to meet their perpetual budget deficits. Charity money is wonderful. It's a true blessing. It should be encouraged and celebrated. But, charity money can be undependable and inconsistent as well. If a church in rural England has a budget problem and delays, reduces, or ends the amount of gift moneys sent to the local Ugandan hospital they have "adopted," the immediate impact of that cutback on the financial status of the Ugandan hospital can be quite painful. Maybe fatal. I've seen empty hospital buildings and abandoned clinics that were set adrift by a decision just like that made in a distant country to stop sending additional charity money to rural Uganda.

Also, it's important to know that cash, in a low-income country like Uganda, is precious. The ability of the co-ops to generate any cash flow at all can be extremely attractive to a Ugandan caregiver. So, the total package of prepaid care and co-op patients has a lot to offer to Ugandan caregivers. We have yet to see a single caregiver summarily turn down a chance to engage in a prepayment relationship. The specific amount of the monthly prepayment is always a topic of intense interest and concern to caregivers for obvious reasons — and some caregivers have rejected specific proposals — but no one has yet said, "Don't bother making a proposal."

Once providers have been approached with the option of working with a plan, they are usually willing to explore in detail exactly what the relationship might mean. Anyone who is already brave enough to deliver care in a 50 percent bad-debt environment isn't going to be particularly intimidated by the possibility of losing some money on prepayment. Particularly when the provider isn't risking cash, but is guaranteeing to provide specific services. Providers know how to deliver services.

Once a general agreement is reached with the caregiver about participation in the plan, the conversation goes very quickly to details. The key detail is obviously the amount of prepayment that the provider will receive. The basic agreement is usually that the caregiver will be paid a specific amount of money each month in exchange for a specific set of available services. The amount paid can be per person in the co-op, or per family, or in some combination of individual and family. That amount to be paid to the provider determines what the co-op will need to charge its members in premium. Setting the premium is both science and art. If it's too high, no one will enroll. If it's too low, that prepaid provider will go broke providing the services. So, the challenge is to get that number "just right." Getting that number right, of course, requires both actuarial science and the fine art of marketing. And the initial efforts in any local co-op always involve a lot of mutual learnings and adjustments. It's generally a good idea to get the local caregivers included in that rate-setting process early so that the caregiver understands completely that charging too much will cause people not to enroll and then the entire program will fail. Caregivers can easily understand that thinking when it's explained clearly to them — and their initial demands for more money can often be very effectively mitigated by involving them as full strategic partners in the rate-setting discussions.

The next issue to be resolved in setting the exact premium and provider prepayment level is usually the specific benefit package — the set of local services — that the provider would be obligated to provide in exchange for the money.

The benefit packages vary a bit from co-op to co-op based on decisions like maternity coverage and co-payments. They also vary from care system to care system because some care systems are more complete than others. It's pretty hard to provide a benefit for X-rays in a hospital with no X-ray machines, for example. Reality rules.

When presenting a short form description of the benefits, the Uganda Health Cooperative staff often says to prospective members, "The benefits include all the care that can be delivered at the local hospital and by the local doctors. Any care that requires another doctor or another hospital is not covered. Here is a list of what is covered."

Those lists create a level of mutual understanding for all parties that is also needed for the co-op and provider partnership to succeed.

A second, directly related, major issue to be negotiated with the caregiver is the "underwriting rules." We talked about those rules in Chapter Four. Caregivers care deeply about those underwriting rules for obvious reasons. Providers in a prepaid plan model are directly at risk. They are, in effect, the insurance company. The composition of the risk pool is therefore very important to them. The providers need real answers to the key underwriting questions. Will quotas be required? What will they be? Will pre-existing condition exclusions be used? For what conditions? How will the co-op work to help the provider have a broad enough spread of risk to make the local risk pool financially viable? These issues and decisions, as noted earlier, fall under the control of each local co-op. They are issues of huge interest to local caregivers, because the amount that the caregivers will charge and the risk they will take on depend on how these decisions are both made and enforced.

The Uganda Health Cooperatives staff helps formulate and mediate those discussions.

The situation is helped a bit by the fact that the local caregivers are not being asked to be at risk for any "out-of-area" care. That benefit limitation helps providers relative to cost exposure but, as noted earlier, it can be a disappointment to plan members if they need a service that isn't locally available.

Again, as noted earlier, one of the downsides of the Ugandan prepayment approach for some members is that it does not yet create a fund to be used to pay out-of-area claims. Why? It's pretty simple. There is no money to pay those claims. Only local care can be covered. Some of the prepaid care sites do, however, make referrals to local specialists when those specialists exist. Those specific referrals are generally covered by the plan. In those cases, the referred specialists are paid directly by the prepaid provider — not by the co-op. Those specialists usually give a financial "good deal" to the primary co-op doctor for the price of their care. In reality, there is generally a good deal of give and take between the prepaid caregiver and the health co-op before the price point is finally set for either member premium or the prepayment amount.

Another key series of discussions between the co-op and the caregiver relates to health improvement programs. Prepayment creates a wonderful incentive for disease prevention. Prepaid care providers, for example, are obviously at risk for the costs of treating malaria. These costs can be significant. So, it is very much in the provider's best interest to keep people from getting the disease. Mosquitoes carry the disease. People get the disease when mosquitoes bite them. That is the only source of malaria. It is, therefore, very much in the best interest of the care system to encourage patients and co-op members to use chemically impregnated mosquito nets to keep people from getting the disease. The physicians know which families have the highest likelihood of getting malaria. Prepaid physicians have a strong financial motive to be particularly persuasive in helping those specific families use the nets. In some cases, the co-ops and caregivers have significantly subsidized the cost of buying those nets in order to save money on malaria care itself.

Likewise, the doctors know that when a child is infected by parasites, the child is often weakened by the resulting anemia. An anemic child is less likely to be able to withstand a case of malaria. So aggressive programs to de-worm the children also can help cut the overall costs of malaria care for the prepaid caregiver.

Remember, in the United States and in Uganda, in a pure fee-for-service model, the providers' sole financial incentive is to provide and bill for individual incidents of care. Every malaria patient with money is actually a direct source of significant revenue for a fee-for-service caregiver. In a fee-for-service world, there are absolutely no financial incentives to help prevent malaria. In a prepaid model, however, every malaria patient is a source of expense — so programs to prevent malaria become financially desirable for the physician caregivers and for the hospital.

Patients, of course, are much better off with prevention. Given an actual choice between good care for a serious illness or not getting sick in the first place, it's pretty easy and logical to choose health.

So helping providers and co-ops set up effective prevention programs is a priority for the local health co-ops and, as you will read later, it is a task now assigned to the staff who work to support all of the co-ops.

Administrative Support

Another important aspect of the relationship between the Uganda Health Cooperatives and the providers is the willingness of the care provider to be the site of, and operator for, the plan computer system. The most effective way of running the plan and keeping records was, we decided, to have a small computer set up at each care site. HealthPartners initially created and provided the software for these computers. It's a very efficient model. The local computer system keeps track of all local care delivered to the plan members. Providers can also use the system to keep track of their other patients at the same time, so some rural Ugandan sites are now actually world leaders in setting up a form of "electronic medical records." Most medical records in Uganda — to the extent that they exist at all — are simple lined sheets of paper (sometimes 5x7 cards) that list only the sketchiest details of patient care. We've seen them stacked in physicians' offices on open shelves in rough alphabetical order. Information is both inherently incomplete and hard to find —

much less easily accessible for group-wide record keeping. So, HealthPartners staff very early in the process built a simple record keeping system for Ugandan providers that basically took the most basic and elementary set of needed patient and member information and computerized it. As noted earlier, the spectacular people at Oracle Corporation took a look at that system, added some engineering, and upgraded it significantly.

The simple but relatively complete new system — thanks to the dedication, commitment, and skill of the Oracle Corporation staff working with the HealthPartners USA staff — keeps track of all care for each patient — drugs, procedures, diagnoses, etc. The system has the ability to price care and report on patterns of care. The system keeps track of which families have mosquito nets and whether or not those families get malaria.

There is probably some irony in the fact that some operational American health care organizations may not have systems as complete and fully integrated as the one now used by some Ugandan care providers.

Issues of data backup, hard copy backup and power blackouts all exist. At this point, early in the process there is a certain rigor in the input to the system — strongly encouraged by the Uganda Health Cooperatives' staff. It is not guaranteed that rigor will continue into the future as the local plans on all sites and levels run with less central support.

In any case, in order to run the plans at the lowest administrative cost, the local mini plans in various Ugandan communities all use the same exact database and machine at each care site.

To date, the computer system has been warmly received in Uganda by multiple parties. Use of the system is not exclusive to HealthPartners or the Uganda Health Cooperatives. It has been made available to a number of other Ugandan health plan startups as they emerge, because we very much wanted to help those plans get started and because HealthPartners wanted the kind of uniform data about diagnosis and care for all local providers available for the kinds of comparative inter-group provider research that is so hard to do in the United States.

At some point — when the system is used widely in multiple Ugandan villages — it may be possible to do longitudinal research on the effects of specific treatments. Ideally, with the right telephone hookups, it might be possible to do some of that research from the United States by pulling medical record and treatment data from desktop computers in the mountains and jungles of Uganda.

In any case, a requirement of contracting with the local care providers for the local co-ops is that the providers must use and maintain the database from that laptop system, making key information available when needed to the co-op leaders.

Improved Health and Best Care

The final requirement for working with specific Uganda health providers is an agreement to work with the Ugandan health care co-ops and HealthPartners on preventing disease, improving health, and improving the consistency and quality of care. HealthPartners' mission is to improve the health of its members, patients, and the community. All programs of the Minnesota plan in Minnesota are aimed — either directly or indirectly — at that goal. In this case, the term community is being used in its broadest sense — the community of human life on our planet.

In Minnesota, HealthPartners has taken a leading role in both disease prevention and care improvement. The "Partners for Better Health" program has set very specific quantifiable disease prevention goals in eight categories of care. Diabetes prevention, for example, is a HealthPartners' goal. So is suicide prevention.

The HealthPartners board of directors has a "Partners for Better Health" committee that meets regularly to provide governance to that comprehensive prevention agenda. It is now recognized as being one of the best disease prevention programs in the world — one of the few with truly aggressive and carefully measured targets and goals for specific areas of prevention.

In each prevention goal area, the Minnesota plan brings together its brightest and best physicians and other excellent and relevant caregivers to figure out how to achieve the goal.

The results have been excellent. In heart care, the HealthPartners score on beta-blocker follow-up (95 percent) far exceeds the national average of less than 70 percent. Diabetic care results — like diabetic nephritis follow-up at 93 percent — far exceeded national averages of less than 35 percent when we started the Ugandan co-ops. Premature births have been cut to less than half of the national average.

Overall, in each area of focus, HealthPartners' systematic, science-based approaches have improved quality and access to best care. That kind of thinking is core to how HealthPartners approaches its mission. Kaiser Permanente, of course, has an equivalent, award-winning prevention program and agenda.

Those same approaches and philosophies that were used in HealthPartners in Minnesota to improve care were later being transferred to and applied in Uganda, as part of the overall agenda. The goal is to use the very best available practices for the care of malaria, for example. Ideally, all doctors participating in each co-op will have information at hand about the best and most effective approaches to malaria care.

In the United States, there are large variations in care practices. That same variation exists in Uganda. When we looked at three Uganda doctors, each used a different protocol for treating malaria patients. Those patients would, we believe, be best served by having all doctors use the best available approach.

How can that be done?

Again, the approach to be used will be to bring the best and brightest Ugandan caregivers together to set goals, and then to do the research necessary to figure out the best way of achieving those goals.

Overall, the care providers of Uganda have impressed us time and again with their commitment, their dedication, their work effort and, in some cases, their personal heroism. They perform great deeds in trying circumstances, and we have felt privileged to work with them. Now, one of our goals is to help those doctors work together to figure out best care practices for Uganda.

In Minnesota, HealthPartners also was the founding partner of the Institute for Clinical Systems Improvement (ICSI) — a joint venture between HealthPartners, the Mayo Clinic and the Park Nicollet Clinic. ICSI is physician led and physician governed. It brings together some of the best minds in health care to figure out medical best practices and then teach them to Minnesota caregivers. Almost all Minnesota physicians and major hospitals are now ICSI members. And the care results have been spectacular. Every major payer in Minnesota has now agreed to accept those physician-developed medical protocols as best care. So, many care outcomes in Minnesota have gone to levels far better than the rest of the country. Collaborative quality improvement programs are relatively rare in other United States communities. Again, I need to mention that Kaiser Permanente has created the Care Management Institute (CMI) to do very similar work for Kaiser Permanente physicians. The Kaiser Permanente results in care management have also been well documented. Getting smart people to work together to achieve best care is obviously a good approach. CMI and ICSI actually collaborate now to some degree. That is breakthrough thinking. The challenge is to extend that kind of collaborative thinking to Uganda. HealthPartners has been working on setting up an "ICSI" for Uganda as part of this initiative.

Chapter Eight
Heroes and Hard Workers
Make It Happen

*Without the right staff, the best plans and
the best strategies are just dreams and memos ...*

$\mathcal{A}$s I noted earlier, one of the first decisions made by
HealthPartners about setting up health care cooperatives in
Uganda was to have all on-site staff be Ugandan. No staff member
based full-time in Uganda is American. Since a major goal is to
have the whole project survive the departure of all American
faces, it seemed logical to start and finish with that Ugandan-only
local structure.

That doesn't mean that the Ugandan staff is entirely on their
own. Americans travel frequently to Uganda to help out. USAID
staff provides local counsel and support as well. Ugandans travel
to the United States for training and skill development relating to
prepayment, plan administration, and disease prevention. But, the
on-site permanent staff at the program is all Ugandan. The
internet gets a lot of use, transferring information and facilitating
communication and dialogue.

The central staff for the project at this point includes a
country director, a nurse/educator, a systems expert, and two

regional co-op set-up workers. For the first two years, the staff was limited to three people. The staff expanded in year four — as we finished our first round of sites and were ready to move more aggressively into new geographic areas.

So what does that staff do?

Overall, the job of the whole staff is to set up new local micro health care co-ops and to support and expand the ones that are in place. The staff interacts with other non-governmental organizations (NGOs), USAID, and Land O'Lakes, as well as with the local caregivers and co-ops. They constantly look for prospective new health care co-ops. When a new prospect is identified, the staff meets with the groups to determine interest. If interested, the staff works with the new potential founding groups to set up the organization and train the members of the leadership group.

The staff also meets with various local care providers to determine interest in becoming a prepaid provider scheme. If interest exists, staff handles the negotiations necessary to put a prepayment contract in place. These negotiations generally have the staff member working as an intermediary for up to a year between the local health care co-ops and the local provider.

Staff members then help both the health care co-op and the providers with the marketing, sales, and promotion efforts necessary to get each co-op started.

Once a program is in place, Uganda Health Cooperatives' staff members help with health improvement programs — running education programs on sanitation, mosquito netting/malaria prevention, and a couple of other carefully targeted, high-leverage health topics.

As the computer system is rolled out to each site, Ugandans on the Uganda Health Cooperatives' staff help train the local care system staff in how to use the system. Uganda Health Cooperatives' staff also review the data that comes from the system for use with the co-op leaders and the care providers. When utilization levels exceed expectations, the Uganda Health Cooperatives' staff helps the co-ops and local providers develop plans to keep the system affordable and the local co-op running. That's obviously a key job — and one that has been particularly well done by the staff.

The Uganda Health Cooperatives' staff also helps plan and create local publicity for the program. Staff members have spent long hours on local radio stations promoting the micro health group and health co-op concepts. I've had a chance to do a couple of those radio shows myself. It's a fascinating experience to be on Ugandan talk radio for an hour at a time. The questions are pretty wide-reaching in their scope and complexity.

The key to staff success anywhere is to pick highly skilled employees with great personal values who are true believers in the mission of the organization. That is particularly true in a pioneering effort like this one. Without the right staff, the best plans and the best strategies are just dreams and memos — neither sufficient to get people needed care. It takes real people with real commitment.

There is no substitute for a true commitment to the goals, mission, and strategy of the project. The ability of the staff members to create trust and cooperation in local areas also depends heavily on their own sense of mission for the project. These are good people. They are doing good work.

Co-Op Leaders Do the Heavy Lifting

The hardest work in the whole process of setting up and running micro health groups and health care co-ops may well be done by the local elected leaders of each group. I can't tell you how impressed I have been with these people. They work incredibly hard to set up each local program and keep it running. The local leaders put their own personal credibility on the line daily. They set up local meetings. They personally talk to people and encourage enrollment. They often walk many kilometers to collect each month's premium. In total, those leaders generally serve as the glue that holds each local group together.

When I was last in Uganda, I asked the local co-op leaders in several sites to describe their role. The term "link" was used several times in different conversations. It's a good and accurate term for a major part of the local leader's role: "Link."

"I'm the link between the national co-op people and our local members," one said. "I'm also the link between our members and the doctor. When our members have problems with the doctor, they come to me and ask me to speak for them."

That's a challenging role — one that the co-op members appreciate.

The co-op leaders are often asked by local co-op members to clarify or resolve problems with the local caregivers. One leader told the story of a physician who began substituting pills for injections for some of his patients.

"Our members thought they were being cheated," the leader said. "They thought that real medicine comes only from injections. They thought the pills were a very inferior treatment.

Uganda Health Cooperatives staff Donata Asaba, Charles Tumwine, and Dr. James.

They asked me to talk to the doctor."

So he did. The doctor explained that the pills were new and better than the shots — and far more convenient for people who needed multiple doses. Those people, the doctor explained, no longer had to walk all day back to the clinic for several consecutive days to get each day's follow-up shot because the rest of the pills could be taken in their home.

The co-op leader heard the doctor, met with the concerned members, and calmed everyone down. Without the co-op leader available to handle that issue, it would probably never have been resolved. Local people would have felt cheated, and the doctor probably wouldn't have had a clue that a credibility problem existed. That's a real additional value. It also took a lot of courage for that local co-op leader to confront the local doctor to talk about what seemed to be a problem.

Link

The co-op leaders interact constantly with the national staff of Uganda Health Cooperatives who are hired by HealthPartners. The local co-op leaders work with the Uganda Health Cooperatives' staff to set up local training sessions on hygiene, disease prevention, and health for co-op members. When members don't pay their premiums, the co-op leaders literally walk to their homes and discuss the issue. More often than not, they persuade members to renew their coverage and pay their premium. Several co-op leaders told me that they spend a lot of time in people's homes having these conversations.

The walking, all by itself, can involve significant distances and time. The walk often isn't easy. The leaders, at this point, are almost all entirely unpaid. They work voluntarily as community leaders to improve their community. They work as parents to create a plan that provides affordable and accessible care for their children. They do it all as a labor of love — a commitment to better local care. It's a pretty impressive commitment.

The program is experimenting now with a small level of payment for some of the leaders. A transportation allowance of some kind is also being considered by some co-ops. If that happens, it will, of course, result in an increase in premium. Premiums in Uganda, as in the United States, are simply the total costs of care plus the costs of administration divided by the number of members. Any added cost therefore increases premium needs. But adding some money to the premium to support the mobility of the local co-op leaders may have merit. It will be interesting to see how that approach impacts the co-ops.

One co-op has already decided to add 500 shillings a quarter to the base premium to create a small transportation allowance for the local leader. Five hundred shillings per quarter is roughly $0.30, on a monthly basis, a dime per family. That may not seem like much until you remember that the total goal for all administrative costs is still about 1200 shillings per quarter.

Interestingly, sales commissions in the United States for insurance agents can run anywhere from 2 to 15 percent of premium, depending on the insurance product. Five hundred shillings is roughly 4 percent of 12,500 shillings. Many United States insurers would be happy to pay 4 percent of premium to cover the costs of sales, member services, and revenue collections. The work done by the co-op leaders covers all of those functions.

Another alternative being considered is to offer some co-op leaders a bike. Most now walk. Bicycles cost roughly $40 in Uganda — about the equivalent of the annual premiums paid by two families. Co-op leaders have to travel relatively long distances to contact everyone who needs to be contacted. They do that now on foot. Or with their own bike. Getting new bikes for co-op leaders might be a better approach and could inspire some people to run for the chair job. It's not clear whether or not that would be a good idea. The current leaders are all in place now because of their strong personal commitment. It might not work as well if any future leaders take the job primarily to get the new bicycle.

In any case, at this point, it's pretty clear that the programs do succeed in most areas primarily because of the dedicated and extensive work done by the local elected co-op leaders.

The challenge will be to help those leaders avoid burnout and loss of interest over time. Without their work and dedication, it would be very difficult to keep some local co-ops going. Creating a self-perpetuating local system requires that those activities all be done every day by someone local. Someone with local credibility and great powers of persuasion.

I have been repeatedly extremely impressed by the commitment, energy, integrity, and leadership of the local co-op boards and chairs. They put their personal credibility on the line as they enroll people into each plan. They take time out of their lives to meet with individual co-op members, with caregivers, and with the national Uganda Health Cooperatives' staff.

When problems happen, they are the first to hear of them, and the first to deal with them. They are, as a group, very impressive people.

Some of the larger co-ops are beginning to name regional sub-chairs to do some of the heavy lifting for subsets of their membership. That's probably a necessary next step in some settings.

As noted above, making the chairmanship a paid job is another alternative, but one that comes with its own risks. Payment might possibly create a different set of motives for the chairs and might even, some chairs tell us, undermine their credibility. It could decrease their sense of moral authority in the eyes of the people who now definitely see them as pure champions of the people and as group leaders. Some co-op members might begin to perceive the chairs to be paid staff, and, therefore, inherently conflicted in their motivations or in some of their decisions. That's an interesting problem. It probably needs to be resolved at each site by each governance group.

In any case, the Uganda Health Cooperatives' central staff from Kampala works very closely with each of the chairs to support their efforts. The chairs do absolutely indispensable work. Selecting the right chair in each co-op setting is a key to ultimate success.

The American Support Staff

Since one major goal of the project was to set up operations in Uganda that would be run, directed, led, and owned on an ongoing basis by Ugandans, we knew that our American support staff had to be selected for skills and abilities that would help us achieve that goal. We also knew that we needed to identify clear rules for the American staff. You might find these rules useful if you are thinking about a similar effect.

We decided to support the Uganda effort by asking existing operational HealthPartners staff to work on the project part time — traveling to Uganda as needed, but living in the United States.

In looking for people to staff and support the Uganda effort, we wanted experienced working people with particular skills, competencies, and approaches to management and development.

For starters, we wanted people who loved teaching — who felt rewarded by teaching. The best teachers measure their own personal worth by their ability to inspire growth in others. We needed people with that mindset to set up the Uganda effort — select and train the staff, and create a team that had the ability to make the Uganda Health Cooperatives an ongoing success.

We knew we couldn't afford to have people in leadership positions who measured their value by their ability and power to control information or function hierarchically. We also didn't want pure theorists — or people whose primary skill set was academic research. We might, however, have been well-served by having at least one additional purely academic researcher on the team to document and measure what we had done, but we opted instead for only pure doers. If we had added a researcher, this book might have been written more formally and sooner by an academic.

We knew we particularly needed people on the project who had skill at hiring other people — managers who knew how to assess both talent and integrity in prospective job candidates. We needed people who could not only hire talented Ugandans, but who could also help them develop — mentors rather than monitors.

We needed people on our United States team with high levels of personal, cultural flexibility — non-judgmental people who could learn from another culture and work to solve problems creatively in the context of that culture. Over the years, in various international settings, we've learned that too many Americans, when in other countries, have a sense that the American way on each topic is the *right* way, and they believe that every local situation must be force-converted to an American model. I learned 20 years ago in setting up a health plan in Jamaica that simply dropping an American solution into another culture or environment could sometimes be hugely counterproductive. I went to Jamaica knowing that the way to run an HMO was to eliminate unnecessary hospital days. I knew that because we had created a successful HMO in Minnesota largely by reducing totally unnecessary hospital days. I had the hammer in hand and went to Jamaica looking for the nail.

When I landed in Kingston, I was ready to set up a stage-one, 1970s-era HMO hospital, pre-admission screening process. The Jamaicans thought I was crazy. What I slowly learned was that actual hospital costs in Jamaica were tiny — pennies, compared to drug costs. Prescription drugs consumed more than 60 percent of total premium dollars collected by the local Jamaican Blue Cross plan. Hospital costs were a dime on the Blue Cross premium dollar. We obviously had to solve the drug problem to create a viable health plan — not fix a non-existent hospital overuse problem. I am repeating that story to make a point.

It isn't easy to leave old American solutions behind when you do business in other countries. But we had to do just that, or we would never succeed.

Another very competent United States health plan that I know went to another African country to set up a plan. The Americans initially decided to impose a tried and true United States rule that forbids local doctors from selling drugs out of their office to their own patients. That's a good rule in the States. That health plan — to control potential conflicts of interest about the sale of drugs by physicians — set up the same rule in Africa, requiring patients to get their prescriptions filled somewhere other than at the office of the doctor who actually wrote the prescription. And that might have worked, if there had been any other places for people to fill prescriptions in their local areas. The only source of drugs in most areas was the physicians' offices. So, patients in those areas literally couldn't get their medications — another case of an American idea transplanted into a setting where it really didn't fit. It took over a year for that plan to learn what they had done and fix the problem.

In Uganda, we needed people who could look to see what actual Ugandan opportunities and problems existed — not people looking to impose American solutions and approaches.

We ended up with local plans that pay their premiums in milk, coffee beans, tea leaves and baby goats. We found ourselves helping burial societies become health societies. We needed people who could look at each local situation with clear vision — not old-school, American-health-solution vision.

At the same time, we needed people who were very technically skilled in all of the functions of a health plan — contracting, network development, claims processing, marketing, rating, underwriting, and administrative operations. We needed people who knew all of the pieces of the American managed care toolkit but were flexible in thinking about which of those tools might be relevant to Uganda. No single person has that entire set of skills — so we used bits and pieces of several people's talents and time to put the program together.

We also knew that we needed a management style for Uganda that featured team-building rather than hierarchical management-by-directive. We needed people whose personal values and integrity were obvious, consistent and dependable — people who could generate cross-cultural trust.

People who work across cultures often start from a position of mutual suspicion, if not actual active distrust. Until they make the real human-to-human connections on a person-to-person level, people tend to automatically interact and interrelate to a large degree based on their stereotypes and presuppositions. It takes personal interaction to move past the stereotypes to full communication, cooperation, and trust.

Some very bright, well-intentioned people do not have the personality or communication skills to create that level of interaction and trust. As we selected American staff to support Uganda, we knew we needed those attributes in each of the people involved or we would have, at best, a distant, formal, and somewhat distrustful relationship with our Ugandan staff members.

As Ugandans visited the United States for training, they met with staff from every major area of HealthPartners. We brought them to Minnesota, in part, so that they could interact with the American support team in their homes and personal environments. We wanted both personal and professional connections to maximize our ability to work together.

As we put together a support team, we started with a list of macro tasks. We needed people to:

- Recruit Uganda Health Cooperatives' staff
- Train Uganda Health Cooperatives' staff
- Create teamwork — both for Uganda Health Cooperatives' staff and between our plans
- Learn Ugandan problems, situations, and opportunities
- Solve problems
- Create communication channels and processes
- Design contracts
- Negotiate contracts
- Facilitate local co-op setups
- Set up simple and elegant administrative systems
- Manage administrative systems
- Invent new tools where needed
- Create financial models
- Set up a relevant actuarial and underwriting toolkit
- Set up health prevention programs
- Assist with quality assurance programs

This is not a complete list of involved areas, but rather a starting point.

The initial role of the American staff was to serve as catalysts. The ongoing role is to provide support. I believe in this model. And, at this point, it seems to work.

If another organization decides to help other developing countries set up micro health plans, I would recommend that they look for American support staff with similar attributes to those I've outlined above.

Chapter Nine
Keeping the Co-Op's Money Safe

Simplicity is strength in cash flow as well as administration.

One major concern relative to any premium-based program in a poor country is that the money collected by the program might be stolen. Within the last decade, several other insurance schemes in Uganda ended up with exactly that outcome. (*Scheme* is a word Ugandans use instead of *plan* when they talk about the co-ops. But the word doesn't carry the negative connotation that it does in this country.) People stole the money. Hucksters made promises to people in villages about life insurance or health insurance. They collected local premiums and then disappeared. We heard that story in several settings. That's one reason why the small set of plans that we support are almost the only vehicle for health insurance in rural parts of the country right now. That's also why people tend to very much dislike giving anyone else their money today based on promises of future benefits. Trust is, for good reason, a major problem. So how does the Ugandan health cooperative model avoid those problems? In part by creating a "reserve-free" approach to cash flow and provider payment. You can't steal a reserve that doesn't exist.

Most people in the United States think of all insurance

processes as inherently and invariably involving the creation and maintenance of significant cash accounts and substantial cash reserves. There's a reason why people believe that. It's true. Anyone trying to start an insurance company or health plan in the United States would need to begin with a pot of cash that could create financial reserves sufficient to meet both United States licensing law requirements as well as the concerns of the health care actuaries and accountants whose job is to estimate the potential impact of future costs.

Claims-based, fee-for-service payment systems, in particular, need large pots of carefully reserved cash on hand at all times — cash needed in the future to pay for all of the claims being incurred now.

Premiums in Uganda Create an Obligation, Not a Bank Account

Having had some experience working with other developing countries — and having heard Ugandan advisors warn us about the temptations that can result even for good people from bank accounts full of relatively unprotected money — one of our major goals was to set up a program that had the cleanest and simplest possible cash flow and the barest and most minimal set of actual opportunities for anyone to actually abscond with any of the cash.

Again, provider prepayment helps immensely. Cash coming into the co-ops isn't held somewhere by the co-op to pay future claims. It's paid quickly and directly to the provider as a prepaid advance against future care. The money, therefore, immediately creates a future service obligation, not a current bank account. That is a key concept — use the money to create an obligation for care rather than a constant temptation. The provider — with all cash in his or her hand — is then contractually obligated to provide that full set of agreed-upon health services and benefits for the members for whatever time period is covered by the contract and paid for by the prepaid cash. Providers are not very likely to skip town with that cash. It's hard for a hospital to run away. Doctors tend not to run off with funds. Also, the cash supply is a bit limited. Prepayment is done a month at a time — or, at best, a quarter at a time. So, the amount of cash held at any one time by the provider is also probably not enough to be a moral hazard.

How does the money get to the contracted providers? In some cases, the existing agricultural co-ops simply deduct part of the weekly milk flow or part of the monthly tea crop and they pay the providers directly — agricultural co-op to care system.

In other cases, the co-op leader and his or her deputies collect the premium and give it directly to the caregiver. That transaction happens very quickly. The premium levels are set at a simple-to-calculate level that allows everyone concerned to know immediately if any money is missing. The micro credit groups are already set up to collect and transmit cash, so that premium flow process is also quick, elegant, and transparent.

The goal is to get the money out of risk and into its all-important work of creating provider obligation as quickly as possible. The providers, themselves, have the actual membership roster and the computer system that tells them which members are currently paid. Individual members know also whether or not their premiums are paid. The receptionist at the doctor's office or hospital checks the computer system whenever each person in the co-op receives care. If, in a worst case, a co-op leader had absconded with a family's premium, the likelihood is that it would be detected very quickly through that clinic visit process. To date, it has not happened. The process is both simple and transparent.

If these Ugandan micro health systems are ever forced to introduce after-the-fact, American-style claims payment mechanisms into the care financing process at some future point, that change would add significant administrative burden and require the creation of cash reserves to pay those claims. Market complexities and pressures or even future government regulations may force that product change to happen at some point. It isn't something that plans should do lightly, however, because that complexity could come with a major price at multiple levels. Any time significant cash reserves exist in a low-income environment, they create an unfortunate temptation that is better avoided than policed.

One additional thought — the whole process very often relies on the premium collection being done by the various co-op leaders. As noted earlier, those leaders are elected by their peers. They tend to be community leaders — trusted by other members of each community. People in Uganda tend to stay in the same community for generations. So the likelihood of a co-op leader running off some month with the co-op's current money is, we believe, minimized by both the process in place and because the kind of people who are elected by their peers to serve in these positions of responsibility tend to be very trustworthy people.

The combination of respected leaders handling the money, fixed and easy-to-calculate premiums, an immediate transfer of cash to providers, and an absence of accumulated cash reserves in the co-op itself all work together to make the co-ops relatively theft-free enterprises.

Because the process is so simple, it's easy to explain to co-op members, and it's easy for them to monitor its operation. Don't underestimate the importance of these factors. The care providers also like the process, watch it closely, and are a good watchdog relative to any delays or discrepancies in cash flow.

Simplicity is strength in cash flow as well as administration.

Chapter Ten
The Model Evolves

We wanted to learn how to help local caregivers
in rural developing country settings.

When we started the Uganda health co-op project, we originally intended to work only with co-ops — consumer-run organizations — providing logistical and operational support only to the purest form of co-op systems in Uganda. That position has evolved over time. We have also now helped several small provider-owned health plans get started in a couple of communities. Why did our position evolve? Because there was a real need for our support from those caregivers, and because we were already there, in position to help. We supported the creation of some provider-owned plans because we strongly believe that Ugandan patients are much better off when they have any viable health plan option available. As you might expect, in the areas when those non-co-op, provider-owned plans have been started, they are also usually the only local health plan that exists. The fact that they come to exist at all, we believe, is a very good thing for the people who live in these communities.

Ninety-nine percent of Ugandans have no private health insurance plan of any kind. When care is delivered, people must pay directly for that care. As we learned early in our look at

Uganda, a serious illness can quickly destroy the finances of a family — often forcing the sale of irreplaceable land or the family's only milk-producing goats or cows to pay the doctor or hospital bill. All Ugandans can theoretically receive care directly from free government institutions, but the government itself admits that it doesn't have enough hospitals and clinics to provide care for most citizens. The government is trying to improve and expand that system, but it will take decades of work and billions of tax shillings to get government-owned care within 40 kilometers of most Ugandans.

So people need alternatives to the tiny and overworked government care system. Unfortunately, at this stage of development, real insurance choices don't exist. In most areas of the country, in fact, the only available way of buying prepaid care is through the tiny local plans that are just beginning to form.

So, the HealthPartners team expanded its mission after the first year to help both small rural hospitals and local physicians start their own plans — plans owned by the caregivers, not by the co-ops. HealthPartners also provided computer systems, technical support, and administrative expertise to those health care providers and their fledgling plans.

Provider-Owned Plans Must Agree to Contract with Health Care Co-Ops in the Area

Working with provider-owned health plans was a logical extension of the mission for us. As I said, when we originally arrived in Uganda in 1997, we were focused exclusively on creating health care co-ops — not generic provider-owned health care plans. We changed that exclusivity requirement relatively quickly for three reasons. First, we believe Ugandans desperately need more plans than a pure co-op market can quickly provide. Second, we concluded that our preferred small local health care co-ops in many locations would already have a much better chance of buying good, prepaid care when the local providers are already organized to provide that care on a prepaid basis. And finally, we wanted to learn how to help local caregivers in rural developing country settings form health plans so that what we learned could also be of service to more people in various areas of the world where co-ops were not a viable alternative. Caregiver-owned plans are, in themselves, another perfectly good model of creating prepaid care.

Co-ops are still the top priority for HealthPartners in Uganda. As we had hoped when we began to help set up provider-owned plans, we have found, in a couple of settings, that it actually can be quite a bit easier to start a co-op as a local purchasing arrangement when a local provider-run plan already exists. Frankly, it's easier for a local co-op to just be a pure buyer in some cases if the local care provider is set up to sell services on a prepaid basis.

In keeping with our underlying commitment to cooperative care models, we attached one major condition to our efforts to help each and every non-co-op, provider-owned plan get off the ground. We insisted that those provider-owned plans each be readily and enthusiastically available in the future to contract with new local consumer-run co-ops, and their members, as soon as we, or others, managed to help those new little co-ops come into existence in each local setting.

In other words, the primary underlying requirement that we tie to our support of those new provider-owned health plans is that they will each do business with any local health care purchasing co-op that later decides to begin operations in the provider's service area. If the local provider group meets basic standards for care, and agrees to form a health plan that will serve co-op customers as well as people they directly enroll, we have been more than willing to help them get started.

That has turned out to be a good strategy. Our decision to help non-co-op provider-run plans helped us get a couple of small, co-op programs underway that would never have begun under an exclusively consumer co-op approach. In each case, the availability of the local provider-owned plan made it easier, a year later, for us to help a local, pure-purchasing co-op get started. So, we do believe our strategy was valid. Doctors and hospitals are absolutely logical health plan owners and founders. Some of the most creative approaches have been set up under that model.

One Ugandan doctor, for example, impressed us with his vision of providing prepaid, prevention-focused care to the children in boarding schools. As noted earlier, Uganda has no public school systems, so parents have to buy education from private schools. Because mass transportation doesn't exist in most of the country, many of the schools are boarding schools. Parents work very hard to scrape together enough money to enroll their children in those schools.

In the boarding schools, the children often have absolutely no health care. If they become ill, they often treat themselves — or manage to somehow get to a local free clinic, if any exist. They may or may not receive care. We heard repeated stories of children with malaria who simply lay in their bunks in the dorms trying to recover while their classmates went off to class. More than once, when the classmates returned from class, the untreated children with malaria were dead in their dorm room.

So, that Ugandan doctor had a vision of adding only 3,500 shillings to each school's tuition charge ($2 per month) and then using that money to provide prepaid medical care to those children whose schools were in his geographic area. He wanted to offer early interventions, transportation when needed, and all necessary care for those children.

He wasn't technically a co-op, but it was pretty hard not to offer him assistance when he asked. He personally ended up using mosquito netting and screens in the dorms where the children slept to significantly reduce the rate of malaria for those children.

Meeting with Dr. Elioda Tumwesigye, a physician at Bushenyi
Medical Centre. Dr. Eli helped stop the spread of malaria by
putting mosquito nets up in school dormitories.

Other similar situations appeared. An innovative administrator at Nsambya Hospital, and an Irish expatriate doctor practic-
ing at that hospital, wanted to create both a prepaid plan for
urban Kampala patients and a self-insured plan for several large
local employers.

Again, once we looked at their goals, we felt that providing
advice and counsel as well as systems support made sense. So
we did.

So, our second priority after the first year was to help provider-owned and operated health plans get started in Uganda. The
idea was clearly catching on. A number of doctors expressed
interest in starting plans. Local doctors or hospitals, we realized,
could start quite a few plans. A number of care providers clearly
saw the advantages of getting enrolled, prepaid populations of
patients coming to their hospitals or clinics. We have since
learned that a very similar model has actually worked very well
for many years in Brazil to get prepaid and affordable care out to
large numbers of local people who would otherwise be without
coverage at all. We brought some of the learnings from Brazil to
Uganda. After we started helping provider-run plans in Uganda,

we also helped a provider-owned plan get started in Nigeria. That plan is very well led and is quite successful.

In Uganda, we decided that the two models we could support were provider-owned plans and consumer-owned plans. We thought that would be our limit — two acceptable models. Then we were asked to expand that rule to work directly with a local government-owned care site. We agreed. As a result, we then also helped one government hospital near Kampala start a government-owned plan. That program has also been a success. It is, in part, the site where the Ugandan Women's Co-Op buys its pre-paid care. So who does that leave out as people to help? We had no reason or interest in supporting any investor-owned or insurer-owned health plans. We didn't want this to be a business instead of a mission. That was a decision we felt very comfortable about. Insurers have their own resources, in any case, and would not need us.

We also decided that the best way to help all of those brand new start-ups learn from each other and work cooperatively together was to form and support a Ugandan Health Plan Council, called the Ugandan Community-Based Health Financing Association (UCBHFA). Dr. Peter Cowley, another inspiring visionary, helped set up the council. Peter was the local medical head for a USAID project at the time. He and several other key leaders, movers and shakers, are described in more detail in the *Acknowledgments* section. Without his efforts, none of the Ugandan plans would have been as successful.

The second major way we felt we could help the various other plans get started in Uganda was to provide our new computer systems and our underwriting insurance expertise to other start-ups.

The mini-HMO computer system that we had been building for Uganda was designed for use by local co-ops. As noted earlier, that was successful. It was not very difficult to modify the system to meet the needs of provider-owned plans.

The system-issued photo ID cards, kept track of enrollment and recorded care data and utilization levels. Interestingly, Ugandan care providers have found this system to be useful in keeping track of their non-HMO patients as well. Allowing the system to be used for non-health plan patients was the right decision, but it wasn't an easy one. We wrestled with our evolving role.

One of the concerns we faced relative to helping provider-based health plans get started was trying to balance the long-term interests of the provider and consumers in the process. We believed that the consumers' interests are best served in the long run by having some significant negotiating leverage relative to the care providers. In a purely provider-run plan, we were worried that the consumers could be at the mercy of local monopoly providers for all pricing and benefit issues.

The providers we worked with were all extremely dedicated, warmhearted, and caring people, so our concern was more conceptual than immediate. But, economic power can corrupt — unless that power is somehow balanced. So, we wrestled with how to develop that balance.

That's how we came up with the requirement that any provider-run plan started had to contract with any future co-ops that might emerge in their service area rather than treat them as a competitor. That answer came in part from our American experience with the market. We concluded that it would be a good thing to create some kind of long-term local market leverage in those sites where the plan was owned by the doctor or hospital instead of by a consumer group.

So, our goal and strategy was to organize local "buying groups" in these settings where providers were setting-up plans. We put together new purchasing co-ops whose job wasn't to actually run the entire local plan, but rather to negotiate benefits and best prices on behalf of their members with whoever owned the local plan.

That volume purchasing model, we believed, works better than having no negotiator working on behalf of the local consumers.

In essence, once a provider-owned plan has been created, we help form the equivalent of a local, health-benefit purchasing coalition.

We believe that any significant potential revenue sources can have great leverage, and a good, well-organized local purchasing co-op can have that impact. Also, the cattle owners that form the dairy co-ops tend to be credible citizens in the local community. So any care system that understands how to stay on best terms with the entire community is likely to welcome their involvement, rather than resist it or take advantage of them.

Prepaid care is a good thing for low income people. Having coverage is better than no coverage. Setting up co-op health plans is a great idea. Setting up local provider-run plans is also a big step forward and should be supported.

So that's how the co-op zealots from Minnesota came to help in the creation of a dozen, non-co-op, provider-owned health plans in Uganda — to benefit each community in the most practical, currently available way.

At this point, it seems to be a good approach.

Chapter Eleven
Selling Our Plan

---

*Groups of people in Uganda who hear words
they agree with have a surprisingly pleasant
way of nodding and murmuring assent.*

$\mathcal{L}$istening to Rebecca Joy Batusa talking to a group of
Ugandans and explaining to them why they should enroll in a
co-op always gave me great pleasure.

Joy leads the HealthPartners Ugandan team. She is a Bogandan
trained in Uganda in education and HIV/AIDS prevention, and
she was our first hire. A woman of great conviction, she is fearless
and charming, resolute and persuasive, extremely bright and
incredibly hardworking. She loves the mission of the project and
has done a spectacular job in putting the co-ops together. Plus,
she is really good at what she does.

As the Uganda Health Cooperatives' Country Director, Joy
coordinates the entire project. From her office in Kampala, she
travels constantly to the various rural care sites and works directly
and closely with all of the co-op leaders. She is responsible for
managerial, networking, financial, and administrative processes of
the Uganda Health Cooperatives, and she meets regularly with
Uganda Health Cooperatives' staff to assess progress and the
resolution of issues. Joy also promotes Uganda Health Coopera-

tives to other key organizations in Uganda, meeting with representatives from USAID, the Uganda Ministry of Health, the Uganda Cooperative Based Health Finance Association and potential member groups. She is personally dedicated to advancing human rights and ethics in Uganda and providing hope for the future of her country on multiple levels. Since this project began, she has spoken at international conferences in Denmark, Canada, Israel, the United States, Africa, and the Netherlands.

Typically, the recruitment gatherings where Joy speaks take place outdoors — under some type of shade tree or awning — with some people sitting on chairs and some sitting on the ground. Occasionally the people meet after hours in local school buildings.

"When your baby is sick, what do you do?" Joy asks. "Do you take her to the doctor? No — because today you can't pay that bill. But, with the health plan, the bill is already paid. You can take the sick baby in for care right away. That is good."

Groups of people in Uganda who hear words they agree with have a surprisingly pleasant way of nodding and murmuring assent. The affirmative murmuring sound is hard to describe. Coming from multiple people, it is extremely harmonious.

It's a "hmmmm" sound — voiced with a positive lilt.

Joy Batusa describes the co-op model.

Marketing the health plan from the back of a truck.

When Joy is on a rhetorical roll, "hmmms" fill the room. She stops at the end of almost every key sentence to let the "hmmms" be voiced. They invariably are heard. Why? The message is solid. Providing health care for your children is a universal desire. It resonates. It sells. Joy goes from site-to-site meeting with people and telling them the story of what's possible if they can just band together to form their own co-op. When there are enough "hmmms," the actual organization efforts begin.

Other members of the staff make similar presentations. Staff members meet with the local dairy co-ops, tea co-ops, burial societies, etc., to explain in clear terms the advantages of becoming a health care co-op.

Those group presentations by members of staff and by local co-op leaders are combined with brochures, posters, organized word of mouth, and, when possible, an amazing advertising approach that relies on a local entertainment group to get the point across.

One of the promotional techniques used in some parts of Uganda is "Voice of Africa" — a traveling theatre group. I personally very much enjoyed seeing "Voice of Africa" in action.

The "Voice" is a small and very talented troupe of actors, singers, dancers, and magicians who travel from town-to-town in a nicely designed large truck. The truck opens up to form a stage for the actors.

At scheduled and well-publicized times, the truck drives into a community and people gather. We've seen hundreds of people in a very rural audience. With no local television, no movie theaters, and limited access to radio, this troupe has little competition as a local entertainment attraction. People gather from many miles around to see the show.

The actors and singers are enormously talented. They sing love songs, do dances, tell jokes, and then, periodically, they do a skit or make a commercial pitch on behalf of a sponsor.

When I saw them perform, our two co-sponsors for the truck show were a barbed wired company and a condom promoter. The barbed wire advertising skit involved an amorous bull (two actors in a bull costume) who was seriously pestering two local cows (also actors in cow costumes). The bull was successful until the barbed wire arrived to fence the bull away from the cow. The bull's response was heartbreaking. The point was clearly made — with fairly direct humor.

The skit selling us involved a mother who couldn't get her sick and dying child to the doctor until she joined the health plan. That skit was heartbreaking, with no humor, but with a heartwarming moment when the mother got her HealthPartners of Uganda ID card and could then finally take her sick child to the doctor for lifesaving medical care. Not subtle. But, pretty honest. And also, very clear.

The condom ad was a lecture on HIV/AIDS — a clear and persuasive piece about dying because protection hadn't been used. Also a graphic piece. Not funny at all.

Between the ads, the entertainers entertained. They were very talented. Admission, I was surprised to learn, was free. How could that happen? How did the actors survive? They were paid entirely by the advertisers.

One of the Americans present said, "Wow, we don't have anything like that in the United States."

He was corrected by another American who said, "We have exactly that. In the United States, it's called commercial TV. Audiences watch American TV shows free because the advertisers pay for the airtime. It's exactly the same business model. Here, it happens on a truck instead of a picture tube."

Exactly. In Africa, the troupe of actors does a great job of getting the message out about the benefits of the health plan.

That's just one small piece of the promotional effort. The overall marketing approach in Uganda is fairly comprehensive in each community, with efforts and programs intended to create local interest and local credibility. The focus is always on the members of the target organization — the milk co-op or friend-ship society that is being recruited as the foundational unit for the health care co-op.

A lot of meetings are held. Groups discuss the co-op model, the benefit set, the costs, and the provider choice. Lots of people talk. It's a very collaborative process. Communications are very clear. No one is confused about what exactly is being proposed or offered. This isn't a process that depends on a memo and a brochure. It's very much people-to-people, person-to-person.

The Big Kick-Off

One of the major promotional and educational events for each new co-op is the kick-off celebration, which I described briefly in the introduction to this book. At that celebration, the first ID cards are passed out for the village. It's a pretty big deal. The usual pattern is to have speeches by the local member of Parliament, the local council chair, the local co-op leader and any members of our United States staff or Uganda staff who can be present. The speeches are all about affordable, accessible, needed health care, and the local people who worked hard to make that care possible.

Usually, music follows. Village choirs are the rule. More often than not, a welcoming song is written for the occasion. A typical lyric might be "Welcome Scott Aebischer to our village, we are so glad you are here. Scott, you are wonderful. Scott, you are great. Scott, we thank you for coming to our village." That last particular lyric can be repeated an amazing number of times. It's quite a pleasant feeling to be publicly serenaded. That's not an experience health plan executives often have in the United States health care world.

Then, as a grand finale, at each opening ceremony, the ranking dignitary and the local co-op leader go to the microphone. (There's always a portable, battery-operated sound system.) The leaders then read off the names of each family who has enrolled in the plan.

Each head of the family comes forward and receives the official family ID card. Handshakes, hugs, and applause are the rule at that point. Everyone celebrates having access to care. People are proud to walk away from the microphone with that new ID card. The ceremonies tend to end with the Ugandan National Anthem and a long walk home for most of the celebrants.

The whole process generates an immense amount of goodwill and adds to the local credibility of the plan. There's usually a small surge in enrollment immediately after the kick-off ceremony.

For obvious reasons, it's important that a major ongoing promoter for each local plan be the local care provider. Enrollment is enhanced and the local co-op gains considerable credibility when the area's primary caregiver speaks well of the co-op.

The entire promotional agenda is well thought-out for each village. Long before the co-op is formed, early fliers are passed out by the local dairy co-op, tea co-op, burial society, etc. The fliers usually announce the concept and call for an initial meeting. Key co-op leaders meet with HealthPartners Uganda staff one-on-one before the meeting to get grounded in the issues and messages. Small meetings are set up so the co-op members' issues can be voiced and the staff can both hear and be heard. And then, when the time is right, a larger meeting is held to get the entire group to decide whether or not to proceed. That whole process can take several months.

As each group decides to go forward, the co-op selects its leaders and the next round of co-op-led meetings begins to make the various decisions outlined in this book. Those meetings are supported by Uganda Health Cooperatives' staff. Once the full set of decisions are made, brochures are printed and another large meeting is set up to announce the results and seek group approval. If the group agrees, then the enrollment campaign begins in earnest. That campaign generally involves extensive discussions between the co-op leader and co-op members. People enroll one-by-one and family-by-family until the magical quota number is achieved. When that happens, the local provider is notified, the members are invited to the kick-off meeting, the ID cards are issued, and the celebration begins.

The key to success for the whole process is open communication and group disclosure — transparency, candor, and commitment. All questions need to be answered. Honesty is an absolute key ingredient. Any falsehood has far-reaching ramifications. People who have been repeatedly cheated and lied to in the past are, of course, on full alert for any sign of lying or deception. Honest people are needed as staff members. The staff selected to do these jobs has to be made up of true believers who are persuasive, articulate, and entirely, completely honest.

The process also has to be respectful of the community and its people. Cultures vary from tribe-to-tribe, village-to-village. Each local culture has to be obviously and openly respected. Caring has to be felt and understood by the group.

When the whole process is done well, informed people come together in mutual trust to create the new plans. That process needs to be choreographed, but not manipulated.

In the end, the plans that result start with the right momentum and the right chemistry to succeed. And, to get the process started, it's important to get off on the right foot. That's why those first meetings are so important.

Also, for us Americans, listening to Joy tell the story is worth the cost of the trip.

Hmmmm.

Chapter Twelve
The Hospital on Bushenyi Hill

---

*An amazing testament to what local people
can do given the right opportunities.*

On the top of a Buhweju District mountain, 35 kilometers from the nearest electricity, 45 kilometers from what used to be the nearest care, and several thousand feet over the moist and fertile local flat land, members of a two-year-old tea-leaf-based health care cooperative have actually built a tiny hospital and clinic. I visited the site just before I left HealthPartners. The local tea farmers had hand-carried both sand and water up the mountainside to build the hospital. They baked thousands of red bricks and then used those bricks to assemble a five-room building with a tin roof. That building now contains two maternity beds, five acute care beds, a tiny delivery room, one wire bassinet, and a table and chair in an exam room that also serves as a laboratory for doing malaria tests. The new care site has no electricity and no running water. The only lighting comes in through open windows. Flashlights are used after dark. The beds have clean, flat surfaces, but no mattresses or blankets.

But, the site does have a physician and a nurse. And clean water. It takes care of people who really need care. It exists only because of the tea growers' co-op.

The Bushenyi Medical Center (BMC) — a private hospital and clinic 45 kilometers away — has contracted with the tea co-op to provide a doctor and nurse every day for that clinic. They agreed to provide that care on top of Bushenyi Hill because the co-op members who live on the steep hillsides surrounding the clinic have each agreed to set aside a portion of their tea harvest each month to pre-pay BMC for that care. Care arrived on that remote mountaintop only because the new co-op gave people a way to pay for that care.

A hospital with bare bunks for beds, no electricity, and hand-carried water may not seem like much to Americans. But, before that Bushenyi Hill Clinic existed, every person in the area who needed significant levels of care had to be carried down the mountain on wicker stretchers. As I noted earlier, those stretchers doubled as local hearses — sometimes on the same trip. The road is steep, rock strewn and very slippery in the rain. Uganda has two rainy seasons each year. Carrying a stretcher down that steep mountain on a wet day is not a journey for the faint of heart, or for people who need care quickly.

Now babies are delivered, minor surgery is performed, malaria is treated, and broken limbs are repaired on the mountaintop.

Also, now that the Bushenyi Hill Co-Op Hospital and Clinic is in place, the people who are in the most dire straits have a new and more convenient access to the Bushenyi Hospital 45 kilometers away. The co-op has also created the area's first real "ambulance" service. Taxicabs do the work. The health plan members who built the clinic building have collectively pooled part of the money they earn from selling their tea leaves to purchase a small solar-powered two-way radio. That radio lets the doctor on the hill call down to the main clinic to have a local taxicab come up the narrow, deeply rutted and sharply winding road to pick up the most severely ill patients. The co-op now pays for that otherwise totally unaffordable taxi ride for seriously ill co-op members. It's part of the co-op benefit package.

Women having difficult labor were the first patients to use that service. The local taxis are small, dirty and definitely not new, but they are a massive improvement over an open wicker stretcher and a 12-hour carry. Particularly, as I noted, in the rainy season.

"Rain Harvest" Water Tank

That particular tea-funded health care co-op has also installed a "rain harvest" water tank and gutter system to take advantage of the rainy seasons and collect clean water off the tin roof of the clinic. Until that tank was built, any water brought to the clinic — or to the tea growers' small homes on the mountainside — had to be hand-carried, usually in bright yellow 20 gallon plastic jugs. The new, co-op-funded "rain harvest" process saves a lot of carrying. Fresh water is also an obvious asset for patient care. Uganda is blessed with ample rain. The new rainwater-harvesting system uses metal gutters placed at the edge of the all metal clinic roof to divert rain water into a large storage tank. That relatively clean source of water helps treat patients in the clinic.

Similar rain harvest tanks will soon be built in several local co-op members' homes, with the goal of reducing the parasite infections and dysentery that come all too often from the nearby highly polluted small river that is otherwise the primary source of water for the tea growers and their families.

The co-op is encouraging the development of those water harvest tanks as part of the disease prevention agenda for the health plan and is helping to fund the construction.

Before the tea co-op existed, there was absolutely no disease prevention agenda on Bushenyi Hill. Now there is a carefully thought-out plan that is already making real improvements in local health.

Preventing Disease Is a Top Priority

The number one health care problem in Uganda is malaria. It kills far more Ugandans than HIV/AIDS. Over 90 percent of

Ugandans have had malaria at least once.

Malaria in Uganda is spread almost exclusively by a night-flying mosquito. These mosquitoes are particularly plentiful in the rainy season. In the two rainy seasons each year, mosquitoes thrive in the puddles that form. Malaria epidemics often follow. The disease weakens most Ugandans and kills many thousands — with children most vulnerable to dying. Children who are already anemic from other common, local parasites are at the very highest risk.

Now, because the health care co-op is in place, if you look into the houses of many co-op members on top of that mountain, you will also see large, rectangular fine-meshed mosquito nets suspended over many of the beds. The nets are permanently impregnated with a chemical that kills mosquitoes. (The chemical used on the nets is a natural extract from the chrysanthemum flower.) Because homes in rural Uganda have no screens or glass in the windows, these nets create the only place that the community members can go to avoid the mosquitoes.

Initial data indicates that the new nets have cut the incidence of malaria in that co-op by more than half.

So, at the top of the Bushenyi Mountain, because a small health care co-op was formed, there is now a tiny hospital, a miniscule clinic, a medical transportation service, a malaria prevention program, and better access to safe water. It's totally self-governed and totally self-financed. There is no charity care on the top of that hill.

The local tea farmers own the care site as a co-op. Those same farmers "own" and lead the local mini health plan. Those farmers, as a group, make the key decisions about their benefits, their care sites, their premium levels, and their care.

Life is better for entire families because the co-op exists on the top of that hill.

No portion of that care system — except for the warmth, caring, and personal skills of the wonderful medical and nursing

Putting the first piece of roofing on for the new hospital.

staff — would meet minimum standards of care anywhere in the United States. But those standards are not relevant on the top of that mountain. The whole effort has to be seen in the perspective of local reality. In Bushenyi, that care site is a blessing and a miracle. More than 100 people walked up to 15 kilometers one way — mostly uphill — for the grand opening. Singers, dancers, drummers, and local politicians made the opening day a memorable and festive occasion.

A key part of the celebration was the sense by the community that they were helping themselves because the co-op that was the foundation for the new and improved care was not a charity, but a local organization that the co-op members governed and owned.

A Guide Book, Not a Rule Book

This book was written to help people think about setting up similar cooperatives and micro health plans in places other than Uganda. It was intended to be both a story about an idea and a guidebook — a partial implementation manual of sorts. My goal was to describe some of the underlying principals used to run the plans, along with some of the specific tools needed to get similar health plans started.

Starting a co-op health plan — or micro health "scheme" as our Ugandan friends sometimes term it — offers some obvious immediate challenges. Issues need to be addressed and resolved. There are actuarial issues, administrative issues, training and marketing issues, cash flow challenges, care delivery challenges, and major communications and continuity problems. Current funding for health care in the areas served by the co-ops is almost always overwhelmingly inadequate. The local care system is slender, fragile, heroic, and overworked.

Total health care spending in Uganda averages about $12 per person per year. There is one doctor for every 18,450 patients. There is no government health plan — although the government does try very hard to set up its own hospitals and medical groups in various areas of the country. Technically, the government is responsible for everyone's health care. Budget constraints make that obligation pretty much impossible to achieve.

Uganda is not a place where either standard European health financing models or typical American health financing approaches have much chance of success at this point in Ugandan history. The co-op approach is designed to fit into that harsh, but clear, economic reality — to create what leverage can be built around local people who want better health care. Local heroes have made local co-ops possible.

Offsetting the immense problems involved in setting up these little health care co-ops is an immense, compelling, and totally understandable desire by many Ugandans to provide affordable health care to their children, families, and community.

Also offsetting these problems is an obvious desire by the heroic and overworked Ugandan caregivers — hospitals and physicians — to make care accessible and affordable for their patients.

Into that setting, the HealthPartners staff brought many decades of experience with just about every variation of American insurance and prepaid systems. That experience was coupled with a strong commitment to the concept and practice of cooperative health care organizations, buying groups, and risk-sharing plans. Some parts of these several decades of United States-based comparative health experience have, we believe, proved to be both relevant and useful to local communities in the "Pearl of Africa."

Premium For Pennies

If you measure by American dollars, the insurance coverage that has been created in Uganda by the new health care cooperatives is a miraculous value. Premiums run 12,000-20,000 shillings for a family of four for three months. Each additional family member usually costs about 2,500 shillings. The exchange rate, at the time we started the plan, was roughly 1,700 shillings for one United States dollar. So our initial health care coverage cost less than 50 cents a month for each person. By contrast, coverage in the United States often now runs more than $200 a month per person.

That's an amazing cost difference. It's interesting to break it down into comparable terms. American health plan premiums are now roughly 27 cents per person per hour. Uganda health plan premiums, when I last personally worked with the plans, were only 49 cents per person per month. The contrasts are stunning. And, a bit humbling.

In the United States, of course, health plans have to buy care at American prices. A routine day in a United States hospital can easily cost $4,000. Many United States hospitals now charge $5,000 to $10,000 for a day of care. A few charge $20,000 a day — and more. By comparison, a private room at Ishaka Hospital in southern Uganda costs 5,000 shillings a day, or about $3. The care delivered in the United States for $4,000 a day is, of course, very different from the hospital care in Uganda that costs $3 a day. But the $3 a day hospital care has saved a lot of lives. It's a pretty good deal when the alternative is a dirty mat on the muddy ground and no caregivers in sight.

Medical care cost differences are almost equally extreme, and also amazing. A Ugandan doctor working in a government hospital will be paid roughly $500 a month. A United States doctor — right out of medical school and residency program — will be paid $120,000–$360,000 per year, depending on specialty. So, it's possible to buy medical care in Uganda for a lot less money. Premium — in both the United States and Uganda — is simply based on the cost of care. In the United States or Uganda, plans compute premium by adding up the costs of care and dividing by the total number of members. In Uganda, the care costs a lot less. So, a health plan in Uganda can charge a lot less for coverage.

What HealthPartners has done in a few rural areas of one African country may or may not have wider application in some other part of the world. Each local setting has its own unique characteristics that may or may not lend itself to approaches similar to the ones described in this book. This book does not offer this model of co-op-based micro health units as a cookie cutter for international care. I only offer the story as an example of what seems to work in this particular place at this point in time.

It is my hope, however, that some of what we've learned in Uganda might prove to be useful to you as a reader in some other comparable setting.

What Have We Learned?

So what have we learned in setting up tiny health care co-ops in the heart of equatorial Africa?

We learned that people everywhere want health care for their kids and are willing to work both hard and cooperatively to make that happen.

We learned that caregivers in those kinds of impoverished areas can be really good partners in creating community-based health care programs.

We learned that prevention really does work, and that caregivers who are prepaid can do very creative, patient-focused things to help patients avoid malaria, avoid dysentery, and avoid the complications of problem pregnancies.

We learned that local people, given the right tools, can set up self-perpetuating prepayment programs with local providers of care in ways that work for both the provider and the patient.

We learned that care providers everywhere share an inconsistency of practice patterns that aren't always optimal for patient care. (See *Epidemic of Care* and *Strong Medicine* for a United States perspective on that issue.)

We learned that many parts of the American insurance underwriting and benefit design tools and concepts can be transformed in useful ways for decision making by small health care co-ops whose leaders are sometimes illiterate and whose members are almost all breathtakingly poor.

What are we still debating about this approach?

We're not entirely sure about the "no charity" rule. It's hard to hold ourselves to that standard. We very much wanted the local health plans to be self-sustaining — not subsidized in any way by charity money. It seems to work. But, it's a very painful rule to maintain. It probably does have a real impact on how well providers deal with prepayment — but it's a really hard rule to follow, when we have resources and those resources are so badly needed in Uganda.

We're also not sure about the role of reinsurance to help with the occasional epidemic, and its cost impact on prepaid caregivers. Some form of reinsurance probably makes sense — but having the reinsurance kick-in at 120 percent of total cost obviously creates a major physician incentive to spend more than 20 percent beyond capitation — adding costs as quickly as possible to get to the richer pot of money. A disease-specific reinsurance approach probably makes the most sense — with malaria as the key disease to be reinsured.

We're not sure about the best way to continuously support the continuing formation of the micro health co-ops. They can be self-sustaining, once started, but they do take expertise and skill to be initially organized and set up properly. They don't just happen.

Brazil and Chile

I spent some time in both Brazil and Chile looking at the variations of local health plans in those countries. Both were fascinating. The Chilean model didn't seem as directly applicable, but some portions of the Brazilian model looked a lot like the provider-instigated and owned health plans we helped start in Uganda. More than 1,000 small, prepaid health plans have sprung up in various Brazilian towns, villages, and communities — all built by local care providers on the basis of locally available care. As near as I could tell from talking to local caregivers and government officials, none of the Brazilian mini-plans had a consumer co-op base. The government of Brazil was wrestling with the issue of how to regulate those plans. It seemed to me that excessive regulation by the Brazilian government could potentially drive more than a few of those small but thriving local plans into extinction.

It wasn't at all clear whether various local populations in Brazil would be better off without their small local plan. Some policy leaders argued that the gap that was left would be filled nicely by much larger and better capitalized national and multi-national insurers. That may be true. I doubt it, however, because the local mini-plans were set up to be very much local niche products — and the large national plans didn't seem to have the potential to reach out to each and every niche.

I could be wrong. It was a fascinating learning experience to spend time looking at these plans.

I've also talked to people from India about some micro plans that have been forming there. Again, not co-op plans as such. The micro credit groups of Bangladesh, however, seem to come from that particular market context, and the health plans they are trying to create might be fairly similar to the Ugandan micro credit centralized health plans.

So, I can't speak with any comfort about the existence of the pure consumer co-op model in any setting other than Uganda. But, there do seem to be some similar local prepaid approaches evolving from various micro credit groups in a number of settings.

If that's true, that may well be enough to create a workable co-op model that could have some relevance in other developing country settings.

Urban United States

Interestingly, it's not impossible to imagine some relevancy for that cooperation model in some of the inner cities of the United States. Building very local, consumer-run health care co-ops might well turn out to be a viable program for certain United States urban settings. If those very local plans were supported with some workable external infrastructure, they could well serve as a mechanism for very local health care reform. The idea is worth exploring. It would require some very progressive legislation to permit local models to form. It could be very interesting to have some of the same underwriting and coverage discussions in urban America that we had in rural Uganda.

In The End

Overall, the Uganda effort has been a success. People are receiving care. The model works.

It's not entirely clear whether or not that co-op model would work anywhere else — but it's worth thinking about. The little hospital on the top of the mountain is an amazing testament to what local people can do given the right opportunities.

I hope this book was useful. Be well.

Epilogue

They celebrated in typical Ugandan fashion,
with lots of singing and dancing.

$\mathcal{M}$uch has happened in Uganda since we first set out to establish the health care co-ops there. HealthPartners' Scott Aebischer, who I introduced you to in Chapter One, remains actively involved with the Uganda Health Cooperatives, traveling there twice a year to provide oversight to the program, get updated on the project's frontline progress, and learn of any new developments.

In October 2006, Scott had the honor of attending the Uganda Health Cooperatives' first annual meeting for all members. He was a guest at the ceremony held to celebrate the ongoing success of the co-ops. They celebrated in typical Ugandan fashion, with lots of singing and dancing. Staff members handed out certificates, and everyone heard testimonials about what the scheme had done for them. Attendees also watched skits on health-related topics.

This event represented a milestone of sorts. According to Scott, Uganda currently has roughly 6,000 to 7,000 Uganda Health Cooperatives members who have direct coverage. Uganda Health Cooperatives has also helped other co-ops get started that don't work directly with them. So all together, there may be almost

25,000 Ugandans currently receiving health care thanks to cooperative thinking and the hard work of the Uganda Health Cooperatives.

Also, Uganda Health Cooperatives helped create an association, the Uganda Community-Based Health Financing Association (UCBFHA), for all the various new health care schemes in Uganda, most of which have been created through the hospitals scattered throughout the country. The association's mission is to help newly formed co-ops learn the ropes regarding what does and doesn't work, and to provide support and training.

HealthPartners is still helping to set up new co-ops in Uganda, but their focus has shifted somewhat. They're now using the local co-ops as vehicles specifically to help improve health care in areas such as maternal and child health, malaria treatment, and other areas that need attention. In that effort, they received a new grant called the Uganda Health Cooperative of Child Survival Grant, which is funded through the USAID health division's Child Survival division.

Local political stability remains an area of concern for the Uganda Health Cooperatives and HealthPartners. The southern part of the country where they have set up most of their co-ops remains relatively safe, but they had to abandon attempts to establish co-ops in the north because of security concerns.

Everyone involved in the project, from day one, had one major goal in mind: to bring affordable health care to the people of Uganda. I'm proud to have played a small part in making that a reality. The real test of whether or not the effort was worthwhile is the impact it has on individual people in Uganda. The following letter from one of the members tells a pretty typical story. You might find the thoughts in the member's own words interesting.

Health Scheme Story by Asaph Tumwesigye

It was in November 1999, when Donna visited our village at the sub-county headquarters and found us in a local council meeting. She talked to us about the health scheme and how it worked. At this point in time, we did not join the scheme because my group had not yet made a decision. As Donna kept checking on our group, another meeting was scheduled to take place at the parish level. In this meeting, members of my group (Bumbire Abategaya, a Coffee Cooperative Society) decided to join the scheme, and agreed to pay their money (premiums) starting January 2000, with 11 families. I enrolled nine members of my family under this Bumbire Abategaya group. A health scheme committee was formed, of which I became chairman, with another seven committee members.

We were given a chance to select a provider of our choice, and we selected Bushenyi Medical Centre (BMC). We met with the BMC management, together with HealthPartners staff, to negotiate premiums and the package and thus agreed on UShs.12,000 (shillings) per family comprised of four members. Also, if a member wanted to enroll, but did not have a family, he/

Asaph Tumwesigye and his children with Charles Tumwine of the Uganda Health Cooperatives.

she still had to pay UShs.12,000 (shillings). But by then, there was a difficulty in collecting premiums from the rest of the members because they had not yet realized the importance of the health scheme. So we had to keep educating them.

In 2001, four of my kids fell sick due to the malaria outbreak, but this happened in such a way that the first two became sick, and I took them to BMC and got admitted on spot. Two days after, another two children also fell sick, and when I took them to BMC they were also admitted. So I had four children in hospital at the same time.

Six days after they had received treatment and were much better, the nurses and doctors decided to discharge them. Before we were discharged, I was given a hospital bill of UShs.85,000 (shillings). But because I was a health scheme member, I presented my membership identity card and the receipt to show that I had paid premiums. I was then requested to pay only UShs.2,000 (shillings) as a co-payment, after which the kids were discharged. Meanwhile back home, the people in Kihunda were getting ready to buy some of my property like the land and goats because they very well knew that I was not going to manage paying for the hospital bill. When I returned home with my kids, many of these villagers approached me and asked how I managed to solve such a big problem. I explained to them how this was made possible by paying our money ahead of time before we fell sick, and, in fact, this has encouraged most of my village members to join the health scheme.

From that time when I was faced with this problem, I find the health scheme setup a good idea, because we have low incomes and cannot afford to pay for bills individually. In fact, from the time when my family first enrolled till today, I now have five people in this plan because the other four kids have now joined secondary where they too have a similar setup for their schools with BMC.

Also, because sickness cannot give notice, I must be prepared by paying my money in time so that I avoid selling my property, especially like my land, which I am securing for my children. When I pay this money, I become very free because I know that when my family member falls sick I do not have to mind looking for money to pay for the bills because I know that it is already at the hospital. Another thing is that my family members have become friendly with the hospital staff, so even if I do not accompany them there, I am sure they are given the treatment they deserve. Many times, we have been getting trainings like on malaria, water purification, scheme management, how to form health cooperatives, scheme sustainability (because our fear is that suppose one time the founders go away, the scheme should not end there) and many other trainings. So through what I have experienced, I vow not to fail to pay premiums for my family.

Acknowledgments

They have made their piece of the world a better place.

$\mathcal{T}$his project has involved a whole parade of heroes whose dedication took us from the initial exploratory trip to seeing our first patients ... in only one year! One year stunned people. In Washington, they expected us to take two years just to evaluate the situation, including funding a feasibility study followed by a multi-year, incremental rollout supported by a much larger staff. But we focused on getting things done — not on writing plans and assessments.

One big reason for the success: the entire HealthPartners staff was made up of operational people who get things done for a living. We each had a strong predisposition to action — assessment, strategy, and then action. It was not an academic or theoretical team. We built an immediate action plan, hit the ground running and managed to get the initial job done quickly — working with a very small, highly focused, highly skilled, hardworking staff.

Our United States staff made a big difference, but the staff on the ground in Uganda made it all very real. All of the staff on this project are the reason that thousands of men, women, and children who weren't getting needed care in Uganda now receive that care.

I'd like to acknowledge and send my deepest thanks to several individuals who made this happen.

On the American Side

First and foremost, I want to thank **Scott Aebischer**, who accomplished amazing things in Uganda while holding down a full-time job at HealthPartners in Minnesota. You can read more about Scott in Chapter One. Also inside HealthPartners, back in Minnesota, we had two employees who made large contributions to the program: **Jennifer Wenborg** assisted Scott in his coordination efforts; **Maureen Peterson** served as an ongoing liaison with USAID and Land O'Lakes, making sure all of our paperwork got completed correctly and on time — that's no small asset when dealing with governmental issues.

I need to also note that the whole systems project would have gone nowhere without former HealthPartners employee **Greg Dosedel**. He personally built the first version of the computer micro system, and then traveled to Uganda to install it on-site. He then worked with Oracle Corporation to co-develop the later, more sophisticated version. Greg is truly the father of the Uganda mini-HMO system.

Tony Pascaretto, the regional manager of Oracle Corporation, also deserves special recognition for his commitment to a good cause. His willingness to assign local Oracle Corporation staff gratis to the systems project showed a real dedication to doing good work for a great cause.

Dr. Peter Cowley is the medical godfather of this effort. Peter was already on the ground in Uganda as a local medical leader of a USAID project. He is a man of great vision and boundless energy and his unflagging enthusiasm kept the project going in some of the more tenuous early days.

The USAID chief of health at that time, **Jay Anderson**, was a key factor in our success. Jay took more than a week out of his schedule to travel the country with us — looking at the potential care sites, meeting with the dairy co-ops, and providing invaluable insight into both Uganda and the mechanisms of our own

Heroes who made it happen, Dr. Peter Cowley and Scott Aebischer.

government. He is a wise, warm-hearted, and experienced man whose counsel proved invaluable to the project. He has since moved to another assignment. He is a credit to our country and has done a lot of good for a lot of people in a lot of places.

Another superstar for the initial project was **Kathy Horgan**, the Land O'Lakes employee directly responsible for the Uganda dairy co-ops, as well as a number of similar projects in other developing countries. Kathy has unstoppable energy and a huge commitment to helping other people improve their lives. She deserves a whole book written just about her own adventures and achievements.

I mention all of these people because they very directly made the project succeed. Other people, like **Martha Cashman**, the former vice president for overseas projects for Land O'Lakes, also had to be on board for the project to even get started. The great vision and powerful commitment of **John Gherty**, then president and chief executive officer of Land O'Lakes, in starting all of those dairy co-ops in so many countries, was the catalyst for the whole project. John deserves his own spot in heaven for all the good he has done in multiple countries through his leadership for those many co-op transplantation projects.

Thanks also go to **Drs. Maureen Reed and Jim Hart**, who made that first trip to Uganda with us in September 1997. Their insights into the local care situation proved invaluable. They also helped immensely in creating immediate credibility with local caregivers.

On the Ugandan Side

We couldn't have pulled this off without the expertise and enthusiasm of **Rebecca Joy Batusa (Joy)**. She was our first hire, and she was spectacular. Her story is in Chapter Eleven. The second Ugandan employee we hired, after Joy, was **Donata Asaba**, an incredibly dedicated, committed, and persuasive woman. A nurse midwife, Donata ran our health-improvement campaigns and helped set up co-ops in remote areas. Where Joy is the daughter of an Anglican rector at the Kampala Cathedral (a city kid, so to speak), Donata comes from a very rural area on the border between Uganda and Rwanda. She has a great comfort level with rural life and is fearless about going alone into the mountains or jungles to set up programs.

At one point in her career, Donata had a job that involved riding a motor scooter through jungle areas to care for mothers in the bush. She was mentioned in the book *The Man With the Key Has Gone!* (by Ian Clarke) — cited for her courage. This impressive woman has since moved on to a public health assignment with another organization.

Donata was primarily responsible for developing and implementing the Uganda Health Cooperatives preventive care program. The prevention program covers a range of initiatives from improving sanitation and hygiene to reducing the incidence of malaria, the leading cause of mortality in Uganda. More than 90 percent of Ugandans have suffered from malaria, and individuals miss an average of 13 days of work or school a year as a result. One of the initiatives Uganda Health Cooperatives worked on was the distribution of insecticide-treated bed nets to health plan members. These bed nets greatly reduce the incidence of malaria. Donata helped to develop the finance plan for the cost of the bed nets (fees are shared between members and providers), and she worked on the design and implementation of bed-net distribution.

Richard Bakojja, the Ugandan who was then head of the Land O'Lakes dairy project, was another hero of the effort. Richard put his personal credibility on the line in meeting after meeting — telling the dairy co-op leaders and members that they could actually trust the "muzungu" from the USA who were trying to help.

I'm not entirely sure of the literal translation of "muzungu" but Ugandans generally smile when we call ourselves that. I think it's a good thing.

Richard took us from mud huts to the palace of a king — and people always received him as a friend. Richard later became a political leader on a larger scale and helped the president of Uganda with his most recent re-election campaign.

Stephen Baryahirwa, a database consultant in Uganda, is a part-time staff member with Uganda Health Cooperatives. Stephen installs the Uganda Health Information System and trains provider staff on how to verify membership, record health care treatment, produce reports, and analyze the resulting data. Stephen also provides ongoing system support.

The provider community in Uganda also supplied its heroes for the project. **Barbara Ssamula**, a senior administrator at St. Francis Hospital-Nsambya, in Kampala, also worked closely with us to get this project off the ground in Kampala. **Dr. Elioda Tumwesigye**, an expert physician and visionary leader at Bushenyi Medical Center, was a major catalyst in getting comparable physician-led plans started.

Dr. Alvin Rocero, from the hospital in Ishaka in the Bushenyi district, also a superb local leader in this whole effort, was the provider catalyst for our first actual site. Without his commitment and support, that site would never have happened.

Each of those physician leaders has not only worked closely with our co-ops, but they have also set up their own complementary programs to enroll other people in their communities. Any visitors to Uganda who look at these programs will be doing themselves a disservice if they don't spend time with those people.

Dr. Habomugisha, the administrator at Naguru Health Center, also has been a visionary. Naguru is a government hospital, so we originally believed that we couldn't work with them. Dr. Habomugisha figured out how to get the job done and then that hospital became the primary care site for our Kirinya women's cooperative.

The list goes on and on. I can't do justice to everyone involved, but I can say thank you to each and every one for their great efforts. They have made their piece of the world a better place.

Index

Acquired immune deficiency syndrome
(AIDS), 14, 134, 141. *See also*
Human immunodeficiency virus
(HIV)
coordination of benefits and, 58–59
as pre-existing condition, 53
spread through families, 61–62
Actors, health care plan promotion by,
133–135
Actuarial viability/soundness, 29–31,
41–44
as health care co-op goal, 24, 27,
28–31, 41–44
quotas and, 47–48
Administration. *See also* Management
caregivers in, 91, 101–103
as health care co-op goal, 24, 31–32
of HealthPartners, 64
of post-payment model, 81–83, 95
premium collection in, 119–122
of prepayment models, 77–89, 83–
85, 95
reducing costs of, 63–76
of service benefit model, 86–89
of Ugandan health care plans, 68–
74, 74–76
Advertising, of Ugandan health care
plans, 134–135, 136–137
Aebischer, Scott, 12–13, 136, 151–152,
158, 159
Affordable care, as health care co-op
goal, 24, 40. *See also* Costs

Africa
health care co-op setup in, 34–36
insurance plan co-payments in, 54–55
African Air Rescue (AAR), health
insurance available from, 58
Agricultural cooperatives (co-ops)
cash flow in, 121
health care co-op setup and, 34–35,
93
Agriculture, in Uganda, 8, 9. *See also*
Cattle; Chickens; Dairy
cooperatives (co-ops)
Ambassadors Council of Freedom From
Hunger, 36
Ambulances, 25
for Bushenyi Medical Center, 140–141
Amin, Idi, 7
Anderson, Jay, 158–159
Asaba, Donata "Donna," 110, 153,
160–161
Availability, as health care co-op goal,
24, 25–26

Bad debts, collecting, 84–85
Bakojja, Richard, 16, 161
Bangladesh, health care co-ops in, 149
Bankruptcy, health care costs and, 2, 9,
17–18, 124, 154–155. *See also*
Budgetable/budgeted costs
Baryahirwa, Stephen, 161
Batusa, Rebecca Joy, 160

health care plan promotion by, 131–133, 138
Benefit coordination, 45, 57–59, 75–76. *See also* Service benefit model
    in post-payment contracting, 81–83
    in prepayment models, 83–85
Benefit maximums/caps, 56–57
    underwriting rules and, 99
Benefits, negotiating, 98–101
Best care, 105
Beta-blocker follow-up, 104
Bicycles, for health care co-op leaders, 112–113
Billing models, 77–89
    administrative costs of, 65–66
    co-payment and, 69
    late payments in, 72
    paperwork reduction in, 67–68, 76
    prepayment versus post-payment, 80–81
Blue Cross/Blue Shield, 85
    Jamaican, 115–116
Boarding schools, health care for children in, 126, 127
Brazil
    health care co-ops in, 148
    provider-owned health care plans in, 127–128
Broken limbs, Bushenyi Hill Clinic treatment of, 140
Budgetable/budgeted costs, as health care co-op goal, 24–25
Buhweju District, 139
Bumbire Abategaya, 153
Burial societies, health care co-op setup and, 36
Bushenyi Hill Clinic, 140
Bushenyi Medical Center (BMC), 139–143, 153–154, 161
Bushenyi schools, 39
Buying groups, 129

Cameras, for photo ID cards, 70, 71, 76
Capitated models, 80, 85. *See also* Prepayment models

Caregiver-owned plans, provider-owned plans and, 125
Caregivers, 91–105, 146–147. *See also* Hospitals; Physicians; Provider contracting
    in administration, 91, 101–103
    health care co-ops and, 123
    local money for, 96–101
    optimizing health care from, 103–105
    partnerships of health care co-ops with, 92–94
    payment for and recruitment of, 77–89
    prepayment of, 91, 92, 95–96
    roles of, 91–93, 144
    underwriting rules and, 99
Care Management Institute (CMI), 105
Care networks, 13, 78–80
Cash flow. *See also* Money; Payments
    in cooperatives, 121–122
    co-payments in, 55
    in fee-for-service models, 95
    health care co-op setup and, 34, 35
    for local health care services, 97–98
    with post-payment contracting, 81–83
    with prepaid contracting, 78–79, 83–85, 95–96, 120–122
    in reducing administrative costs, 65
    in service benefit model, 86
    theft of health care co-op money and, 119
    in Ugandan health care plans, 72, 76
Cash reserves
    in American insurance industry, 120
    preventing theft of, 119–122
Cashman, Martha, 159
Catalysts, American support staff as, 118
Catastrophic illness, in service benefit model, 86
Cattle, in Uganda, 8, 9, 10, 18, 41, 42, 43. *See also* Dairy cooperatives (co-ops)
Central development costs, in Ugandan health care plans, 73
Central staff, 107–108
Chair. *See also* Leadership

Asaph Tumwesigye as, 153–155
  as Ugandan health care plan leader,
    72, 112–113, 113–114
Charity, health care co-ops as, 28
Charity money, 97, 147
Chickens, health care and, 15
Childbirth. *See also* Pregnancy;
    Premature births
  Bushenyi Hill Clinic treatment of,
    140, 141
  coverage issues for, 41–44
Children. *See also* Infant mortality
  of Asaph Tumwesigye, 154, 155
  in families, 60–61
  health care co-ops and, 39–40, 126,
    127, 132, 134
  malaria epidemics and, 142
Chile, health care co-ops in, 148
Cholera, 8
Churchill, Winston, 7
Claims
  administrative costs of filling, 65–66
  cash reserves for, 120
  eliminating, 67–68
  in post-payment contracting, 81–83
  in prepayment models, 83–85
Claims-based billing model
  administrative costs of, 65–66
  prepayment models versus, 68, 73–
    74, 80
  Ugandan health care plan and, 73–
    74, 80
Claims payment mechanisms,
    administrative complexity of, 121–
    122
Clarke, Ian, 160
Clinics
  construction of health care co-op, 38
  co-payments in visiting, 54–55
Coffee cooperatives (co-ops), 153
Collaborative quality improvement
    programs, 105
Commitment, of health care co-op
    leaders, 111–112, 113
Communication, in health care co-op
    promotion, 137–138

Competence, of caregivers, 94
Complete separation model, 78
Computers
  in administrative support, 101–103
  in paperwork elimination, 67–68
  in prepayment contracting, 68, 82,
    128–129
  photo ID cards and, 70, 71
  staffing health care co-ops and, 108–
    109
  tracking premium payments with, 121
  in Ugandan health care plans, 72,
    73, 74–75, 75–76
Condom ads, 134
Congestive heart failure (CHF), service
    benefit model and, 87–88
Consumer focus, of health care co-ops,
    16–20, 21, 33
Consumer-owned plans, health care co-
    ops and, 128, 129
Contracting. *See also* Health care
    contracts; Provider contracting
  benefit maximums in, 56–57
  coordination of benefits and, 57–59
  co-payments in, 54–55
  definition of family in, 59–62
  out-of-area health care in, 55–56
  post-payment, 81–83
  prepaid, 78–79
  provider, 44
  riders in, 53–54
Cooperation, among health-care
    providers, 129–130
Cooperative model, for health care co-
    ops, 33–34
Co-op leaders. *See* Leadership
Coordination of benefits (COB), 45, 57–
    59
Co-payments, 45, 54–55, 154
  administrative costs of, 66
  negotiation of, 68–69
Costs. *See also* Affordable care; Money
  American versus Ugandan medical,
    145–146
  benefit maximums and, 56–57
  budgetable, 24–25

co-payments of, 55
eliminating unnecessary, 27
health care, 2, 8, 9, 17–18, 20–21,
    123–124, 144, 153–154
health insurance, 29–31
negotiating, 98–101
reducing administrative, 31–32, 63–76
reinsurance and, 147
Coverage, formulating rules for, 41–62
Covey, Stephen, 23
Cowley, Peter, 128, 158, 159
Credibility
of caregivers, 94
of health care co-ops, 136
of local leaders, 109–110, 111, 113
Cross-cultural aspects (culture), in
    health care co-op promotion,
    137–138

Dairy cooperatives (co-ops), 3–4, 9–10,
    16–17, 18, 42. See also
    Agricultural cooperatives (co-ops);
    Agriculture; Cattle; Land O'Lakes
health care co-op setup and, 34–35,
    72, 130
Data. See also Records
in administrative support, 102–103
in prepayment contracting, 82
staffing health care co-ops and, 108–
    109
in Ugandan health care plans, 71–
    72, 73, 75–76
Decision-making process, 45, 62
Deductibles, administrative costs of, 66
Dependability, as health care co-op
    goal, 24, 25–26
Dependable income, prepayment as, 96
De-worming, prepayment models and,
    100
Diabetes prevention, 103, 104
Digital cameras, for photo ID cards, 71
Direct employment model, 78–79
Discounts, 24–25
Disease, in Uganda, 8, 14
Disease prevention, incentives for, 83

Disease-specific reinsurance, 147
Donations, to health care co-ops, 27–28
Dosedel, Greg, 158
Dysentery, 8, 14, 141

E-commerce, 73
Education, of health care co-op staff,
    39. See also Training
Electronic processing. See Computers;
    Data
Eligibility, administrative costs of
    determining, 65–66
Employers
group health insurance with, 50–51
insurance quotas by, 48
Engozi Societies, health care co-op
    setup and, 36
Enrollment windows, 45–46
Exclusions, pre-existing condition, 45,
    46, 52–53
Fairness, 45
as goal of health care co-ops, 45
in pre-existing condition exclusions,
    52–53
quotas and, 48
riders and, 53–54
Families
defined, 44, 59–62
in ID cards, 69–71
Family resources, 2, 8, 153–155
Fee discounts, 24–25
Fee-for-service-based insurance model,
    80–81
cash reserves in, 120
prepayment models versus, 95–96,
    100–101
in reducing administrative costs, 65
service benefit model and, 86–87
Financial viability, as health care co-op
    goal, 24, 28–31, 46
Foundational organizations, in health
    care co-op setup, 36–38. See also
    Burial societies; Dairy cooperatives
    (co-ops); "Friendship" societies;
    Micro credit groups; Tea
    cooperatives (co-ops)

Free government institutions, health
care in Uganda via, 124
Fresh water, at Bushenyi Medical
Center, 141
"Friendship" societies, health care co-
op setup and, 36
Funerals, health care co-op setup and, 36

Gherty, John, 159
Gift money, 97. *See also* Charity entries
Gifts, to health care co-ops, 27–28
Goals
American support staff and, 114
fairness in health care co-ops, 45
getting money out of risk, 121
in health care improvement, 103–105
reducing health care program
administration costs, 63–76
staffing health care co-ops and, 109
of this book, 143–145, 146, 149
for Ugandan health care co-ops, 23–
32, 38–39, 40
Good health, rewarding, 55
Goodwill, for health care co-ops, 136
Government
in coordination of benefits, 58–59
in reducing administrative costs, 65
Government health plan, lack of
Ugandan, 144
Government-owned health care, 124, 128
Group health insurance
enrollment in, 45–46
exclusions from, 45, 46, 52–53
fairness in, 45
quotas for, 45, 46–50
screening for, 50–52

Habomugisha, Dr., 162
Halvorson, George C., 6, 12–13, 127
Hart, Jim, 12, 16, 160
Health care contracts, 44, 76. *See also*
Contracting
benefit maximums in, 56–57
coordination of benefits and, 57–59

co-payments in, 54–55
definition of family in, 59–62
out-of-area health care in, 55–56
riders in, 53–54
Health care cooperatives (co-ops). *See
also* Micro health plans
Asaph Tumwesigye and, 153–155
Bushenyi Medical Center and, 139–
143
caregivers in, 91–105
consumer focus of, 16–20, 21, 33
current status of Ugandan, 151–152
definition of family for, 59–62
evolution of Ugandan, 123–130
formulating coverage rules for, 41–62
foundational organizations in setup
of, 36–38
in health care improvement, 103–105
hospitals in, 93–94
ID cards for, 1–2, 63, 66, 69–71,
134, 135, 136
kick-off celebrations for new, 135–138
learning from, 146–148
in Minnesota, 10, 78–79, 103–104,
105
prepayment models for, 77–89
preventing theft of money from, 119–
122
promoting, 131–138
provider-owned plans and, 124–130
rainwater harvesting by, 141
reducing administrative costs of, 63–
76
in rural Uganda, 1–6, 8, 11–12, 93–94
in Seattle, 11
setting goals for, 23–32, 38–39, 40
staff for, 107–118
this book and, 143–145, 146, 149
training staff for, 38–39
Ugandan dairy co-ops and, 34–35
Health care costs. *See* Costs
Health care improvement, 103–105
Health care needs, in Uganda, 8–21
Health care spending, in Uganda, 144
Health improvement programs, 100, 108

Health insurance. *See* Group health
insurance; Individual health
insurance issues; Insurance entries
Health maintenance organizations
(HMOs), 5. *See also* Kaiser
Permanente
care networks and, 13, 78–80
macro tasks in setting up, 117–118
service benefit model and, 88
setting up Jamaican, 115–116
HealthPartners
administrative costs of, 64
administrative support by, 101, 102,
103
American support staff from, 114,
117–118, 158–160
Bushenyi Medical Center and, 139–
143
in evolution of Ugandan health care,
123–130
health care co-op leaders and, 111
health care co-op ownership and,
33–40
in health care improvement, 103–105
Jamaica Plan of, 13, 16, 20–21
organization of, 13, 78–80
prepayment contracting under, 82
promoting health care plans of, 131–
138
in provider contracting, 44, 77–89
service benefit model and, 87, 88–89
staffing of health care co-ops by, 107
staff of, 157, 158–160, 160–162
Ugandan fact-finding mission of, 14–
15, 16–20, 21
Ugandan health care co-ops set up
by, 2–4, 5, 6, 9–15, 23–32, 39–40,
67–68, 123–130, 144–145, 146,
151–152
Health screening, 50–52
Hearses, 25
Heart care, 104
Honesty, in health care co-op
promotion, 137–138
Horgan, Kathy, 159
Hospital care
by caregivers, 92–93, 94

in health care co-ops, 93–94, 144
prepayment for, 96
Hospitals, 8, 14–15, 144. *See also*
Bushenyi Medical Center (BMC);
Caregivers
American versus Ugandan costs of,
145–146
Jamaica Plan and, 115–116
provider-owned plans of, 125–130
Human immunodeficiency virus (HIV),
8, 14, 134, 141
coordination of benefits and, 58–59
as pre-existing condition exclusion, 53
spread through families, 61–62
Human rights, 132

Identification (ID) cards, 1–2, 63, 66,
69–71, 134, 135, 136, 154
administrative costs of, 66
fraudulent use of, 69–70
for non-health-care-plan patients, 129
in prepayment model, 68–71
Immunization levels, in Uganda, 14
Immunizations, 59
Incentives
fostering, 81, 83
prepayment models and preventive-
care, 100–101
reinsurance as, 147
India, health care co-ops in, 148–149
Individual health insurance issues, 50–52
co-payments, 54–55
riders, 53, 54
Infant mortality, in urban Uganda, 2, 8.
See also Children
Initial enrollment quotas, 46–47
Injections, pills versus, 110–111
Institute for Clinical Systems
Improvement (ICSI), 105
Insurance
formulating coverage rules for, 41–62
health care co-ops and, 29–31,
123–124
prepayment as, 96
theft of health care co-op money
and, 119

underwriting rules and, 99
in United States, 29–31, 78–80,
145–146
Insurance agents, commissions for, 112
Insurance policy options, 45
Insurance scams, 26
Integration, of hospital and medical
care, 92
Intestinal parasites, 8
Ishaka, 161

Jamaica Plan, 13, 16, 20–21
support staff in, 115–116
James, Dr., 110

Kaiser Permanente, 5, 79, 82, 88–89
in health care improvement, 104, 105
Kampala, 7–8, 75, 114
government-owned health care in, 128
Kampala Cathedral, 160
Kenya, coordination of benefits in, 58
Kick-off celebration, for new co-ops,
135–138. See also Opening day
ceremony
Kingston, Jamaica, 115
Kirinya Women's Cooperative, 61, 162

Land O'Lakes, 158, 159, 161
dairy co-ops set up by, 3–4, 9–10,
16–17, 18, 34, 42
history of, 10
Kirinya Women's Cooperative and, 61
in Ugandan health care co-op setup,
23, 26, 108
Languages, in Uganda, 19-20
Late payments, in Ugandan health care
plans, 72
Leadership. See also Chair
by caregivers, 92, 94
health care co-op setup and, 34–35,
36–37, 72
in health care plan promotion, 133,
137
key roles of, 74–76

premium collection and, 121–122
staffing health care co-ops and, 108,
109–111, 111–114
support staff for, 114–118
trust in, 121–122
Learning experience, setting up health
care co-ops as, 146–148
Lifespan, in Uganda, 8
Limited coverage, enrollment windows
and, 46
"Links," local health care co-op leaders
as, 110–111, 111–114
Local governance/control, 55–56, 68,
74–76, 79
in administrative support, 101–103
benefit maximums and, 57
by caregivers, 92–93, 94
formulating coverage rules under,
41–44
formulating quotas under, 49–50
as health care co-op goal, 24, 26
and health care co-op ownership,
33–40
health care co-ops under, 123–130
in health care plan promotion, 133,
136–137
health care riders under, 54
premium collection under, 119–122
prepayment models and, 85, 89
staffing health care co-ops and, 108
staff leaders and, 109–111, 111–114
underwriting rules and, 99–100
of volume purchasing, 129–130
Local money, for caregivers, 96–101
Local services, by caregivers, 96–101
Longhorn cattle, 42, 43

Maintenance, of health care co-ops,
26–28
Malaria, 8, 14, 83, 154, 155
Bushenyi Medical Center and, 140,
141–142
computers and, 102
improving treatments of, 104–105
prepayment models and, 100–101
reinsurance and, 147

service benefit model and, 86
treating children with, 126, 127
Management. *See also* Administration
by American support staff, 117
of health care co-ops, 26–28, 39
of prepayment models, 77–89
Managers, as support staff, 115
Man With the Key Has Gone, The
(Clarke), 160
Maternity coverage, 41–44
pre-existing condition exclusions
from, 52–53
in service benefit model, 86
Matooke, 8, 18
Mayo Clinic, 105
Medicaid, 65
Medical care, by caregivers, 92–93, 94
Medical equipment, in Uganda, 14–15
Medicare, 9, 65
service benefit model and, 87–88
Mentors, as support staff, 115
Micro credit groups, health care co-op
setup and, 35–36
Micro health plans, 2, 35, 40. *See also*
Health care cooperatives (co-ops)
tea co-ops and, 35, 40
Minnesota
health care co-ops in, 10, 78–79,
103–104, 105, 115, 117
HealthPartners staff from, 158–160
Minnesota Cooperative Creameries, 10
Mixed models, 78–79
Money, preventing theft of health care
co-op, 119–122. *See also* Cash
flow; Costs
Monopolies, by health care co-ops, 40
Mosquito nets, 126, 127
at Bushenyi Medical Center, 142
computers and, 102
prepayment models and, 100
"Muzungu," 161

Naguru Health Center, 162
National Public Radio, health care co-
ops and, 5–6
Negotiated fee discounts, 24–25

Negotiation, in provider contracting,
98–101
Nigeria, provider-owned health care
plans in, 128
Non-co-op provider-run plans, health
care co-ops and, 124–130
Non-governmental organizations
(NGOs), staffing health care co-
ops and, 108
Non-health-care-plan patients, keeping
track of, 129
Nonpayment of bills, 84–85
Nsambya Hospital, 8, 127
Nurses, at Bushenyi Medical Center,
139, 140

Objectives, for Ugandan health care co-
ops, 23–32, 38–39, 40. *See also*
Goals
Obligations, with prepayment
premiums, 120–122
Opening day ceremony, at Bushenyi
Medical Center, 143. *See also*
Kick-off celebration
Operating costs, in Ugandan health
care plans, 73
Oracle Corporation, 158
in administrative support, 102
in paperwork reduction, 67–68
Orphans, from spread of HIV/AIDS,
61–62
Out-of-area health care, 55–56
benefit maximums and, 57
underwriting rules and, 99–100
Ownership, of health care co-ops, 33–
40

Paperwork
administrative costs of, 65–67
in post-payment contracting, 81–83
reduction of, 67–68, 68–69, 71, 73,
75–76
Parasites, 8, 14, 141. *See also* Malaria
prepayment models and, 100
Park Nicollet Clinic, 105

Partial prepayment approach, for
caregivers, 92
"Partners for Better Health" committee,
103–104
Partnerships, of co-ops and caregivers,
92–94
Pascaretto, Tony, 158
Payments
for American versus Ugandan
physicians, 146
for health care co-op leaders, 112,
113–114
negotiating, 98–101
Per capita income, in Uganda, 2, 8
Per capita prepayment model, in
reducing administrative costs, 65
Permanente Medical Groups, 79. See
also Kaiser Permanente
Perpetuation, of health care co-ops,
26–28
Peterson, Maureen, 158
Photo identification cards, 69–71, 76.
See also Identification (ID) cards
Physical examinations, in Uganda, 51–52
Physicians. See also Caregivers
at Bushenyi Medical Center, 139, 140
filling prescriptions by, 116
obligations of, 120–122
pay scale of American versus
Ugandan, 146
provider-owned plans of, 125–130
Pills, injections versus, 110–111
Plan/provider relationships, 77–89
in United States, 78–80
Pooling
out-of-area health care and, 55–56
quotas for, 49–50
Post-payment models, 81–83
disadvantages of, 81–83
prepayment versus, 80–81
Poultry. See Chickens
Pre-existing condition exclusions, 45,
46, 52–53. See also Riders
Pregnancy. See also Childbirth
co-payments and, 55
as pre-existing condition, 52, 53

Pregnancy coverage, 41–44
Premature births, 104. See also Childbirth
Premiums
as creating obligations, 120–122
health care co-op leaders and, 111, 112
for Jamaica Plan, 115–116
maximum affordable, 63
payment of, 116
preventing theft of, 119–122
in Ugandan health care plans, 72,
145–146, 153–154, 155
Prenatal care, co-payments and, 55. See
also Pregnancy
Prepaid contracts, 78–79
Prepayment models, 77–89
caregivers in, 91, 92, 95–96
claims-based billing model versus,
68, 73–74
constructing, 83–85
evolution of Ugandan, 123–130
as learning experience, 146–148
local health care money and services
in, 96–101
obligations owing to premiums in,
120–122
post-payment models versus, 80–81,
82–83
promoting in Uganda, 131–138
in reducing administrative costs, 65
service benefit model and, 87, 88–89
staffing health care co-ops and, 108
for Ugandan health care co-ops, 67–
68, 68–74, 74–76
versus fee-for-service models, 95–96
Prescriptions, physicians and, 116
Preventive care, 103–105
at Bushenyi Medical Center, 141–143
by caregivers, 91
incentives for, 83
prepayment models and, 100–101
service benefit model and, 87–88
Primary payers, in coordination of
benefits, 58–59
Pro-active health programs, 83
Promotion, of health care co-ops, 131–
138

Provider contracting, 44. *See also*
    Caregivers; Contracting
  benefit maximums in, 56–57
  coordination of benefits and, 57–59
  co-payments in, 54–55
  definition of family in, 59–62
  evolution of, 123–130
  local health care money and services
    in, 97–101
  obligations owing to premiums in,
    120–122
  out-of-area health care in, 55–56
  payment plans for, 77–89
  riders in, 53–54
  staffing health care co-ops and, 108
  underwriting rules in, 99
Provider-owned plans, health care co-
    ops and, 124–130
Provider-run health plans, 65–66, 73
  local control versus, 26
Publicity, staffing health care co-ops
    and, 109
Purchasing co-ops, 129–130
Quality of care, improving, 103–105
Quotas, 45, 46–50

Radio promotions/shows, staffing health
    care co-ops and, 109
Rain harvest water tank, at Bushenyi
    Medical Center, 141
Records. *See also* Data
  in administrative support, 101–102,
    103
  in prepayment models, 84
  in service benefit model, 86
  in Ugandan health care plans, 74–
    75, 75–76
Reed, Maureen, 12, 16, 160
Reinsurance, 147
Reputation, of caregivers, 94
Researchers, as support staff, 115
Respect, in health care co-op
    promotion, 137–138
Riders, 45, 53–54. *See also* Pre-existing
    condition exclusions

Risk
  definition of family and, 59–60
  insurance plan co-payments and,
    54–55
  out-of-area health care and, 55–56
  removing money from, 121
  in service benefit model, 86
  spreading, 29–31, 45, 47, 48, 49,
    52–53
  underwriting rules and, 99
Rocero, Alvin, 161–162
Rural hospitals, in Uganda, 14–15, 15–16

Sales commissions, for insurance
    agents, 112
Scams, health-care, 26
Schools, health care co-ops and, 39–40
Screening, 50–52
Seattle, Washington, 11
Self-sustainability, as health care co-op
    goal, 24, 26–28, 38–39, 148
Service benefit model, 86–89
*Seven Habits of Highly Effective People,
    The* (Covey), 23
Singers, health care plan promotion by,
    133–135, 136
Skills, of American support staff, 116–
    118
South Africa, health care co-ops for, 5
Specialists, underwriting rules and,
    99–100
Ssamula, Barbara, 161
Stability
  of health care co-ops, 93
  political, 152
Staff, 107–118
  American support, 114–118
  at Bushenyi Medical Center, 142–143
  central, 107–108
  duties of, 108–109, 109–111
  of HealthPartners, 157
  leaders among, 109–111, 111–114
  success of, 109
  training of, 38–39

Standards
  fairness, 45
  underwriting, 44
St. Francis Hospital-Nsambya, 161
St. Paul, Minnesota, 10
Stretchers, 25
  for Bushenyi Hill Clinic, 140, 141
Suicide prevention, 103
Support
  administrative, 101–103
  by American staff, 114–118
  in health care co-ops, 93–94
Sustainability, of health care co-ops,
  26–28

Taxicabs, as ambulances, 140–141
Teachers, as support staff, 114
Tea cooperatives (co-ops)
  Bushenyi Medical Center and, 139–
  140, 142
  health care co-op setup and, 35, 40,
  72
Television, 135
10 percent target, 63–76
Theft-free system, as health care co-op
  goal, 24, 26
Theorists, as support staff, 114–115
Training
  by and of American support staff,
  117–118
  health care co-op leaders and, 111
  of health care co-op staff, 38–39, 108
  in health insurance tools and
  concepts, 62
Transportation allowance, for health
  care co-op leaders, 112
Transportation facilities, Ugandan
  health care and, 25–26
Trust
  by and of American support staff, 117
  in co-op leaders, 121–122
  as health care co-op goal, 24, 32
  in health care co-op promotion,
  137–138
  staffing health care co-ops and, 109

theft of health care co-op money
  and, 119
Tuition, adding medical fees to, 126
Tumwesigye, Asaph, communication
  from, 153–155
Tumwesigye, Elioda, 127, 161
Tumwine, Charles, 110, 153
Typhoid, 8

Uganda
  American support staff in, 114–115
  Bushenyi Medical Center in, 139–
  143
  caregivers in, 91–105
  coordination of benefits in, 57–59
  dairy co-ops in, 3–4, 9–10, 16–17, 42
  definition of family in, 59–62
  disease in, 8, 14
  health care cash flow in, 95–96
  health care co-op ownership in,
  33–40
  health care co-ops in, 1–6, 8, 11–12,
  123–130, 131–138, 145–146,
  146–148, 149, 151–152
  health care needs in, 8–21
  health care program administration
  costs in, 63, 67–68
  health care riders in, 54
  health care spending in, 144
  HealthPartners co-ops in, 2–4, 5, 6,
  9–15, 23–32, 39–40, 67–68, 123–
  130, 144–145, 146
  HealthPartners staff from, 160–162
  health screening in, 51–52
  history and demographics of, 7–8,
  19–20
  hospitals in, 8, 14–15, 15–16
  ID cards in, 1–2, 63, 66, 69–71, 134,
  135, 136
  ID fraud in, 69–70
  immunization levels in, 14
  infant mortality in, 2, 8
  insurance agent commissions in, 112
  insurance plan co-payments in, 54–55
  insurance quotas in, 48–49

level of health care in, 15–16
local health care money and services in, 96–101
micro health plans in, 2, 35, 40
out-of-area health care in, 55–56
paperwork reduction in, 67–68, 68–69, 71, 73, 75–76
paying health care providers in, 77–89
per capita income in, 2, 8
pre-existing condition exclusions in, 53
prepayment for health care in, 68–74
preventing theft of health care co-op money in, 119–122
preventive care in, 103–105
reducing health care costs in, 63–76
staffing health care co-ops in, 107–118
wealth in, 7–8
Uganda Health Cooperative of Child Survival Grant, 152
Uganda Health Cooperatives, 38, 40, 75, 151–152, 153, 160–161
administrative support by, 101, 102–103
American support staff and, 114
health care co-op leaders and, 111, 113, 114
in health care plan promotion, 131–132
in provider contract negotiations, 98–99
staffing health care co-ops and, 108–109, 110
Uganda Ministry of Health, 132
Ugandan Community-Based Health Financing Association (UCBHFA), 128, 132, 152
Ugandan Health Plan Council, 128
Ugandan Women's Co-Op, 128
Underwriting rule issues, 41–62
benefit maximums, 56–57
coordination of benefits, 45, 57–59
co-payments, 45, 54–55
decision making, 45, 62
enrollment rejections, 50–52

enrollment windows, 45–46
fairness in, 45
family definition, 44, 59–62
identifying, 41–44
negotiating, 99
pre-existing condition exclusions, 45, 46, 52–53
providing only local health care, 55–56
quotas, 45, 46–50
riders, 45, 53–54
Underwriting standards, 44
Unexpected medical problems, coverage for, 41–44, 46
United States
advertising in, 135
care networks in, 13, 78–80
clinic construction in, 38
coordination of benefits in, 57–58
enrollment windows in, 46
health care cash flow in, 95, 145–146
health care co-ops in, 10–12, 34, 38, 149
health care costs in, 9
health care program administration costs in, 63–64, 65–67, 76
health care riders in, 54
health insurance in, 29–31, 78–80
HealthPartners staff from, 158–160
health screening in, 50–51
ID fraud in, 69–70
improving health care in, 103, 104,105
insurance agent commissions in, 112
insurance money in, 119–120, 145–146
insurance plan co-payments in, 54
insurance quotas in, 48
Jamaica Plan and, 20–21
medical care in, 15–16, 147
medical computer systems in, 102, 103
paying health care providers in, 77, 78–80
post-payment contracting in, 80–81, 82

pre-existing condition exclusions
      in, 52
prepayment contracting in, 80–81,
      85
preventive-care incentives in,
      100–101
service benefit model in, 87–88
staffing health care co-ops and, 107,
      145–146
support staff from, 114–118
United States Agency for International
      Development (USAID), 4, 27, 128,
      132, 152, 158
staffing health care co-ops and,
      107, 108
Urban United States, health care co-ops
      in, 149

Vaccines, 59
Vertical integration, of hospital and
      medical care, 92–93
Viability, of health care co-ops, 28–31,
      41–62
"Voice of Africa," health care plan
      promotion by, 133–135
Volume purchasing model, 129–130
Water, at Bushenyi Medical Center, 141
Water purification, 155
Wealth, in Uganda, 7–8
Wenborg, Jennifer, 158
Wives. See also Women
   additional, 60
   in spread of HIV/AIDS, 61–62
Women, in health care co-ops, 61. See
      also Wives
Women's Co-Op of Kirinya, 61, 162
World Bank, health care co-ops
      qand, 5–6

About the Author

George C. Halvorson was named chairman and chief executive officer of Kaiser Foundation Health Plan, Inc. and Kaiser Foundation Hospitals, headquartered in Oakland, California, in March 2002. Kaiser Permanente is the nation's largest integrated health plan, serving more than 8.4 million members in nine states and the District of Columbia.

Halvorson has more than 30 years of health care management experience. He was formerly president and CEO of HealthPartners, headquartered in Minneapolis. Prior to joining HealthPartners, he held several senior management positions with Blue Cross and Blue Shield of Minnesota. He was also president of Senior Health Plan, as well as president of Health Accord International, an international HMO management company.

Halvorson serves on a number of boards, including those of America's Health Insurance Plans and the Alliance of Community Health Plans. He is the current president of the board of directors of the International Federation of Health Plans, and a member of the Harvard Kennedy School Healthcare Delivery Policy Program, the Commonwealth Fund Commission on a High Performance Health System, and the new Institute of Medicine Task Force on Evidence-Based Medicine. He also serves on the Executive Council of La Clínica, and on the Ambassadors Council of Freedom From Hunger, an international development organization working in 17 countries. He is a former board member and trustee of the National Cooperative Business Association.

Halvorson is the author of books on health care, including *Epidemic of Care,* published in April 2003, and *Strong Medicine*. He is currently writing two new books, one about racial prejudice around the world, the other about how to systematically reform health care in America. He has written numerous articles on subjects ranging from health information technology to the changing marketplace.

Halvorson has interacted in a number of settings with academics, policy makers, and health industry leaders, including the HR Policy Association, the World Bank, the European Health Care Congress, the National Business Group on Health, the Microsoft Annual Health Plan Executive Forum, the National Governors Association, the World Health Care Congress, and a number of universities and colleges. He has served as an advisor to the governments in Great Britain, Jamaica, Uganda, and Russia on issues of health policy and financing.